LOVE AMONG THE DAUGHTERS

LOVE AMONG THE DAUGHTERS

By
Elspeth Huxley

1968
CHATTO & WINDUS
LONDON

Published by
Chatto and Windus Ltd
42 William IV Street
London W.C.2

★

Clarke, Irwin & Co. Ltd
Toronto

Printed in Great Britain
by Ebenezer Baylis and Son Ltd.
The Trinity Press, Worcester, and London

With love to the surviving daughters
P. and J.

Contents

Chapter One

ENGLAND was always called Home in those days, but it was not. It was a foreign land whose people spoke our language; little else was the same.

To begin with, everything was tiny, almost miniature. Railway carriages were little boxes that you squeezed into instead of clambering up. The train glided away with nothing but a gentle hoot and the flicker of an emerald flag, instead of a great deal of shouting, waving, last-minute boarding and leaping clear, a pandemonium of wails, clanks and hootings, as if a pirate vessel was being boarded in mid-ocean. The quiet English train then passed decorously between rows of tidy, symmetrical, identical and, again, very small houses, their gardens trim and paintwork clean, and women to be seen scrubbing steps. There was an indefinably alien look, perhaps because of the monotony and packed-togetherness. You proceeded into a checker-board of little paddocks, each one separate, and each one incredibly green.

A patchwork-quilt of a country, I thought, like the country Alice ran through with the Red Queen. And the farmyards were like those toy ones with little red and white varnished cows, and stubbly thumb-sized wooden sheep, and trees on stands. Roofs were red and ricks yellow, fields lush with corn, yellow with buttercups or charlock and green, green and again green, the kind of green you could eat, or plunge into like a pool, that almost seemed to live and breathe, it was so vivid. Of course there is green in Africa, especially when young grass comes up after bush fires, but never quite like this, so deep, so rich, like crême-de-menthe.

Despite the tinyness of things, the people looked much the same size as in Africa, and I wondered how they fitted in. The men wore a lot of thick, heavy clothes and the women tight-fitting little hats that came down over their ears like helmets—cloches. We did not have cloches in Africa, only big mushroom-like double terais, or hard cork topees. And of course here

everyone was white—pink really, but we called them white;
even men with shovels working on railway lines and station
porters were Europeans. There were no rickshaws, and no
shaven-headed, dark-bronze women doubled under loads of
firewood. Even smuts from the locomotive smelt quite different;
they were the residue of coal and not of eucalyptus logs.

"I shan't recognize my Aunt Madge," I observed, full of
foreboding, to my travelling companion.

"I may not recognize Edwin," she replied. "The last time
I saw him, he was in a grave."

Maggie and I had shared a cabin all the way from Mombasa
and never quarrelled once, probably because she was an easy-
going, good-natured woman, considerably older than I was;
she had had two husbands already, and was about to espouse a
third. In fact Edwin was to be the next. As it seemed unlikely
that he had been resurrected, I inquired, thinking of Yorick:

"Is he a grave-digger?"

"We'd had a wake, the ground was slippery and he fell in.
He kept shouting 'Wait for me! Wait for me!' and luckily they
did."

"I've only seen my Uncle Jack once. I've absolutely no idea
what he looks like."

On the occasion of our single meeting he had been in uniform.
That was in the First World War. My father had left East
Africa for England to take part; when it became clear that an
early end to these activities was not to be expected, my mother
Tilly had abandoned the farm at Thika and followed Robin, tak-
ing me with her.

We had made our base with Aunt Madge, Tilly's sister, but
had not spent a great deal of time there. Tilly joined the Land
Army, and went about among the lanes and villages of Dorset,
Somerset and Devon on a motor-cycle, dressed in a smock
reaching well below the knee, shiny gaiters and a wide-brimmed
felt hat, seeking recruits. After impassioned speeches in village
halls, shy but sturdy young women would sign on for the land;
in those days they were nearly all domestic servants, and Tilly
said the motor-bike was needed for a quick getaway from
infuriated ladies of the manor whose last kitchen-maid had been
beguiled into exchanging colander for milking bucket. Not that

the motor-bike was to be relied on to get her out of harm's way
quickly; it was temperamental, and Tilly's knowledge of
mechanics negligible, so she spent a lot of time pushing it
doggedly along muddy lanes. Since then, there had been changes
at Nathan's Orchard. Gertrude, the eldest of my three cousins,
had grown up; Kate, the middle one, was in a convent school
and Joanna, the youngest, must have quitted the nursery. The
dogs, I understood, were still there—probably in greater
numbers than ever.

Aunt Madge was at the station to meet me in the pony-cart,
and that at any rate had not changed; it smelt just the same,
of leather and straw, of pony and cowdung and old sacks, and
the stuffing that was coming out of the leather-covered cushions,
and the musty smell of a very old fur rug that shed its hairs on
everything, especially on my aunt's baggy black skirt and
tattered black cardigan. Although not in mourning, she nearly
always wore black, and a squashed-up round felt hat from which
her hair, still golden, escaped in long wisps and tendrils; she
was generally puffing at a cigarette. She had not changed much
either.

"Tilly sent her love," I said.

"I suppose she still enjoys lording it over all those blacks."

"Not lording it exactly." I was thinking of Njombo, who
after every circumcision ceremony brought several sons we
didn't want to be taken on as kitchen *totos*; and of all the
flocks of goats and herds of cattle, banned in theory from our
paddocks, we kept on sighting as they were hurried into bush-
clad gullies and patches of forest.

"You still argue," Aunt Madge retorted. "And you've got
fatter." She sounded cross, but was not really, and added with
a grunt: "Well, you're very welcome, if Nathan's Orchard isn't
too poor and humble for you now that I suppose you've grown
up. I'm sorry to see you're wearing one of these hideous short
skirts."

Maggie had taken me for an intensive, confusing and
theoretically cheap shopping spree at Derry and Toms. This
was the period when hips and breasts were out; every female
suddenly managed to avoid having them, although a few bulges
did appear now and then in what nature held to be the right

places and fashion houses the wrong ones. Luckily I had straightish legs and, reared in shorts, no inhibitions about showing my knees.

"Will Gertrude be at Nathan's Orchard?"

"Gertrude!" my aunt snorted—she was an accomplished and frequent snorter—and flicked the whip at the fat Buttercup, who put her ears back and gave an intentional stumble. "Gertrude's home isn't good enough for her. Or for those stuck-up young men in what she thinks are smart regiments. She only comes home to wash and iron her ridiculous underclothes."

Gertrude had always been my aunt's least favoured daughter. Either because of that, or the other way round, she was Uncle Jack's favourite; she was also the prettiest, in fact more or less a beauty, with wonderfully deep, violet-blue eyes, a perfect skin and clear-cut, well proportioned features. Also she was slim, and had a fashionably straight figure.

"Kate is at home," Aunt Madge remarked, with another snort. Although Kate was often cheeky, disobedient and infuriating, my aunt liked her the best, and Uncle Jack the least, of their daughters.

"I thought she was at school."

"She has been expelled."

As my aunt did not sound really angry, and might even have been faintly amused, I ventured to ask why.

"Insubordination, going out at night and gambling on race-horses."

"Gambling on race-horses isn't exactly a crime."

"It is at a convent. Especially when you start a book and persuade the others to gamble and don't pay out the proper odds on winners."

"Perhaps she did the sums wrong," I suggested.

"She's going to study art." Aunt Madge sounded complacent. In her own eyes my aunt was a champion of the underdog, and perhaps getting sacked by nuns put Kate into this category.

I inquired after Joanna. "At school in Suffolk," Aunt Madge said. "One of those so-called smart places where they learn nothing except how to paint their faces, fall in love with the games mistress and don't get enough to eat. They wear hideous pleated things called gym tunics that show their knock-knees.

Joanna has chilblains all the year round and plays scales on a
broken-down piano for an hour a day. Why, heaven knows. It
was Kitty who insisted on her going there so Kitty must take
the consequences."

Kitty was another aunt, sister to Madge and Tilly, and the
only one comparatively well off—that is, with a financially
successful husband. They lived mainly abroad, and had taken a
fancy to Joanna ever since her infancy. I had no doubt they were
paying for the smart if spartan school in Suffolk. "Always
gadding about," Aunt Madge said, referring to her youngest.
"Kitty is in Athens, and has Joanna for the holidays. She comes
back smelling of garlic." Aunt Madge gave a sort of chortle;
when she did this, and when she smiled, the gaiety and charm
she had possessed in youth, deeply buried now under a layer of
sour resentment, shone through for a moment to beguile and
possibly bedevil her companions. This was the secret of the hold
she still had over people, even members of her family: the
promise of treasure for which you went on digging, even when
you seldom struck anything but rock, clay and old bones.

Nathan's Orchard had got smaller, as all places do that you
have known as a child and return to when childhood is over. It
might have got dirtier, I was not sure. Curtains and carpets
might have faded a bit more. The silver cow with a hole in
the small of its back was still on the revolving book-case in the
sitting-room, the picture of a white sea-eagle hung over the
mantelpiece, damp continued to stain the ceiling near the door,
old copies of the *Wide World* magazine and *The Captain* were
stacked on the lavatory seat—it was a wide mahogany seat,
with a handle that you pulled up to flush the pan—and a smell
of stewing tripe permeated everything. The dogs still lived on
tripe that was still cooked every day. There was one major
change: no more candle-sticks with their snuffers on the table
in the hall. Nathan's Orchard had gone over to electric light.

"Do you remember the corpse candle?" Aunt Madge
chuckled. The corpse candle dated from a time when we had
been obsessed by ghosts. We read all the ghost stories we could
lay our hands on and, of a winter's evening, turned down the
smoky paraffin lamp in the nursery after tea—delicious bread-
and-dripping with onions, raw or pickled according to the time

of year—and made up awful tales, each of us continuing where the last left off, and each determined to make her contribution the most ghoulish, horrible and blood-curdling of the lot. The competitors had been Gertrude, Kate, myself and old nanny Sullivan, who had stayed on to look after Joanna, full of bunions and rheumatics, frequently singing in a cracked voice to an out-of-tune piano ditties such as *When Irish Eyes Are Smiling*, fond of the bottle and stout as a pig.

I used to wake with nightmares, imagining that the ceiling dripped blood. We decided to organize a corpse candle that would, apparently of its own accord, float eerily down the stairs, predicting some awful disaster. This was to affright Aunt Madge and Uncle Jack, who condemned our ghostly tales as unhealthy. We secured, I cannot remember how, an outsize candle, I suppose ecclesiastical. We bored a hole through its middle, slung it on a length of thread and practised lowering it very gently over the balustrade on the landing.

The candle slid about along the thread, turned upside down and behaved as if possessed by a malignant spirit; as soon as we had calmed it down, the thread snapped. We persevered whenever Uncle Jack was safely in his study and Aunt Madge out on the farm. At last the moment came for the *dénouement*. This was to occur after supper, when I was to thrust a haggard face through the drawing-room door and exclaim sepulchrally, "Come quick, there's something on the stairs"; my aunt and uncle were to rush into the darkened hall and see the ghostly flame slowly, and without apparent human aid, float down the stairs.

On the appointed evening the candle was more obstinate than ever, but at last all was ready, with Gertrude holding one end of the thread and Sullivan the other, and Joanna wrapped in a blanket by Nellie the kitchen-maid who came to offer adenoidal and impractical advice. When I opened the sitting-room door, a dog had just been sick on the sofa and my aunt was mopping it up, her ear-rings—pendant pearls—quivering, her cigarette sending up curls of blue smoke. My uncle was seated in a broken-springed arm-chair behind a book, managing in the stiffness of his posture to express silent protest against the dogs, the dirt, my aunt's temper and the general lack of military order and gentlemanly decorum that characterized his home.

"Come quickly," I began. "There's something——"

"Fetch the Jeyes' fluid."

"But on the stairs——"

"Stop arguing, and get the Jeyes!"

"Uncle Jack, please come, there's something . . ."

"You are old enough by now," my uncle said, "to know that it is always wisest to obey your aunt in this house."

Behind me I heard starling-twitters, a gust of giggles, a stage whisper; "Quickly, quickly, it's coming *down* . . ." I flung the door wide open and gave a piercing scream.

My uncle lowered his book, bristling; my aunt bellowed; the dogs were started off. From sofa, chair and rug they rose like angry fountains, suddenly the room was bursting with them and the air shaking with furious sound as they flowed in a yelping cascade into the hall. Aunt Madge followed, laying about her with a riding crop snatched from the top of the bookcase as she strode past. It was all very familiar. When excited, the dogs would often start a fight, although they had been lying hugger-mugger by the fireside a few moments earlier, and it would end in oaths, pandemonium, bites and blood, and pail-fuls of cold water hurled in all directions. In fact my aunt was shouting for water now, and Uncle Jack swearing at the absent Nellie for not lighting the hall lamp, which we had extinguished.

No one noticed the candle-flame which quivered softly for a few moments at the top of the stairs. Then came a crash, and the beam of Uncle Jack's torch revealed a fat white object at his feet.

"What the blazes——"

For once the dogs were not serious; after a scuffle or two, the barking subsided, and they allowed themselves to be driven back to their sofas and chairs. My aunt rounded on me.

"Screaming! You're hysterical. I shall tell your mother to take you away. You'll find yourself in a lunatic asylum at this rate, like Flossy. I suppose it's in the blood. *Now* will you fetch the Jeyes?"

The twittering on the stairs ceased, my uncle went back to his book; I could just see his forehead and the top of his head where his gingery hair receded; he had a trick of sliding back the skin, as if it were detached from the bone and muscle underneath and formed a sort of shield or carapace. By this means he could turn his countenance into a mask to express injured disapproval so unmistakably that no words were needed. Would Aunt Madge go into one of her sulks? They could last up to three weeks.

Now, coming back some ten years later, I wondered if the sulks went on as before. Uncle Jack had grown sparser, bonier, more stooping, more withdrawn; but his voice, precise and gentle, was much the same.

"I hope you had a pleasant journey."

"My father sent his love,"

"It's a pity he didn't stay on in his regiment. Africa should be left to elephants and niggers. Sooner or later the sun's actinic rays rot the cells of the brain."

"Topees and terais . . ."

"The rays enter through the eyes. My men went down like ninepins in Kumasi though no one was allowed to bare his head even in barracks, and church parades were always held before sunrise. The skulls of the Ashantis are three times as thick as a white man's and the frontal bones jut out so as to shield the eye."

Uncle Jack had fought in one of the Ashanti campaigns and had a medal for it, put away in a drawer. It was a pity he could never wear his miniatures. I had worn them once, dressed up for one of our plays. The cases of two German shells stood on the mantelpiece and there was a German officer's helmet in the old servants' hall, which was now our dining room; we presumed that Uncle Jack had slain the owner in single combat.

"Not all their skulls are thicker," I said. "When Chegge got kicked on the head by Lucifer, the doctor said his skull was like an eggshell, and if he had——"

"My God, still arguing," said Aunt Madge. "Don't contradict your uncle and go and get some corn for Buttercup. It's in the granary."

The smell inside the granary was another thing that had not altered. It was rich as the richest Christmas cake, so thick you felt that you could squeeze it between your hands. What was it compounded of? Mature hay, darkened by the ripening process, which smells entirely different from new hay—nutty, fruity, almost like molasses. And molasses too; a cask stood about somewhere. Cottonseed cake that came in big slabs, brittle, oily, you could break it in your hands; we used to feed it into a crushing machine cranked by a handle. Linseed cake too, sharp and resiny and reminding one of cricket bats. Leather—and the sweat of horses that had soaked year after year into big padded collars. Axle grease for wagons; old horse-shoes, cobwebs, mice, hens, wormy woodwork, chaff, pigs, turpentine; and black liquids in black, sticky bottles—drenches for worms, husk and colic. The sharp smell of cider, made from windfalls and honey and maturing in old brandy barrels—Perce said you ought to put an old wagon chain dragged in dung and a dead rat at the bottom of the barrel. At haymaking, they trundled a cask into one of the wagons and took it out to the fields.

The hay made me sneeze with all its little grass-seeds and spiky awns. Names came back: I wondered whether it had been mown in Cornground or Big Owls' Nest or Thickets, and if Perce had pitched it, or young Ted. Ted was the only man under forty who had remained on any of the farms for miles around during the war, except for one or two epileptics. He was one of seven brothers; when the other six had been killed or posted missing, his mother applied for his release because she was a widow, and to everyone's surprise the army let him go.

In ten years Kate had grown from a gawky child to a spindly-legged, in-between-stage girl of seventeen. Her eyes were her best feature. Both the elder sisters had noticeable eyes of deep larkspur blue, large, and able to project an impression of wisdom that was totally misleading. People said they had their mother's eyes. Uncle Jack's were blue also, but much paler, almost ice-blue, or in certain lights grey, and they could be alarming, like pinpoints, like jet nozzles. Anger seemed to concentrate them, but it only clouded Madge's over, Kate's could gleam with malice but also they could soften, and she warmed to helpless things—displaced fledglings, blind baby shrews exposed by the mower, moths caught in spiders' webs; small and suffering creatures were all around, if you noticed them.

"Oh, hallo," Kate said. She was sitting on the kitchen table

2

licking her fingers. "Have some raw pastry. It's much better than when it's cooked."

The kitchen was full of bins and copper saucepans and objects unconnected with cooking, like bottles and buckets and ropes, and sacks and barrels, and tins of turpentine and creosote.

"The last time I saw you," Kate recalled, "you had a pink dress with sequins which I thought ghastly, and Aunt Tilly had a lot of silkworm eggs. Did they ever turn into silkworms? You were reading *Dracula*. And now we've grown up, in a manner of speaking. You heard I got the sack from the nuns?"

"Yes, I'm sorry."

"I wasn't. In fact I had to work like blazes to fix it. The nuns kept forgiving me, so I had to keep on thinking up something else. They wouldn't have sacked me even for the betting if I hadn't hung on to most of the cash. Poor nuns! They tried so hard."

"You'll only get sent somewhere else."

"No, I'm too old, no one will take me."

"Finishing schools?"

"Thank God, they're too expensive. I'm going to study art."

"I'm surprised they let you."

"Aunt Lilli's got a friend who teaches it, and mummy supposes she's respectable. God knows why. Anyway she lives near London, almost in it in fact. So in October . . ."

"You'll spoil your dinner if you keep nibbling." Nellie, now the cook, was taking things in and out of ovens in a big, black, clumsy stove which took twenty minutes and a great deal of shaking, riddling, poking and wastage of matches to start every morning at six o'clock.

"Things taste much nicer in the kitchen, no wonder cooks get fat. You've got fat, Nellie."

"You mind your own business, Miss Kate."

Nellie had gone into service straight from school, at fourteen. She could not be more than twenty-five or six now, although she looked much older; but then a lot had happened to her; or not exactly happened so much as occurred in passing. There was a Christmas morning when I had lain in bed in the cold, hollow back room I always had at Nathan's Orchard—the one whose ceiling had dripped blood—where I could hear the stairs creak-

ing and footsteps padding down the passage towards the
lavatory, and doors rattling, and starlings in the roof, and all
the other sounds you do hear in old houses; I had lit the candle
and was unwrapping things out of a stocking tied to the foot of
the bed. It was one of those times you always remember,
because of the extraordinary shapes of the packages and the
tingling feel they gave your fingers, the rustle of tissue paper,
the smell of the orange in the toe, and the flickering of shadows
on the ceiling, which had so many faces, animals and shapes in
it made by stains of damp; this was a private moment, it was
only later you would exchange and compare.

Unexpected bumps and scrapings occurred overhead, and
sounds came from the other end of the passage. It was too early
for Aunt Madge's tea, even on Christmas morning. I groped
for a dressing gown and went on to the landing. At the far end
was an alcove and a stairway leading to the attic, and someone
was coming down; it proved to be Aunt Madge in a thick blue
dressing gown and dog-chewed bedroom slippers, her long
golden hair in two plaits, a candlestick in hand; several terriers
followed and one sat down to scratch at the foot of the stairs,
thumping against the bare boards.

"What the devil are you doing?" Aunt Madge said crossly
when she saw me staring at her.

"Is something wrong?"

"Mind your own business and go back to bed."

Nanny Sullivan came hobbling down after her, treading sideways to ease the bunions. Her hair was down too, but fell all
round in grey wisps, like a scruffy silver halo.

"Just look at the child, with no slippers," she exclaimed,
"picking up splinters and chilblains. Back to bed with you, my
darling, and a merry Christmas to us all."

"Christmas!" Aunt Madge gave a snort even more aggrieved
than usual. "What a time to choose! Just like that beastly little
slut."

"Little pitchers have long ears." Sullivan was always quoting
old saws like that. She was especially fond of the one about the
wind changing, and if you were squinting, putting out your
tongue or making faces, you would stay like that for the rest of
your life. I went back to my presents, the candlelight and, later,

the gradual draining of darkness from the room, beyond the window a ragged lemon sky, the tugging of a blustery wind against many bare branches, the distant throaty haow-haow-haow-ing of Perce to summon his cows to their milking shed, and smells of frosted mud and morning smoke and frying bacon. A brittle skin of ice lay over ruts and puddles, and we should have scrambled eggs for breakfast. Presently Kate looked in and we compared the contents of our stockings, which never quite fulfilled the promise of their shapes.

"What was all the commotion?"

"Only Nellie," Kate replied. "She had a baby in the box-room."

The boxroom made it seem funny, so we both giggled, thinking of the baby in a box, but unable to imagine that it had anything to do with Nellie.

"Nanny says it's a shrimp." That sent us into more fits of giggles, thinking of long whiskers and jutting eyes, and nets and rocks and spray. Despite the war, we had been to Westward Ho! a place that seemed wonderful to me because of Kingsley's romance and the exclamation mark, even though it had rained most of the time.

Since that Christmas, Nellie had produced a number of babies; several had died, but Kate said there were three survivors who were boarded out with an uncle nearby. It was good of Nellie's uncle, I remarked, to take in her three little bastards. I could just recall the uncle, who had a wispy moustache and a watery eye; every year he used to take his niece for a week's holiday at a boarding house in Bournemouth.

"They're all his," Kate explained.

Chapter Two

GERTRUDE arrived a few days later. She was nineteen, and did not spend much time at Nathan's Orchard. While no one at the farm lacked food, warmth or shelter, my aunt and uncle could not keep up with the county, and did not try. Everyone was reconciled to this but Gertrude, who lived a nerve-racked and nomadic life of country house-parties, hunt balls, London balls, race meetings, and events revolving round names familiar to everyone but me such as Lord's, Henley, Wimbledon, Cowes, Ascot and Goodwood, each connected with a sport of some kind. These place-names amounted to a sort of shorthand that, if you lacked, rendered you practically unable to converse at all in those circles.

One of the difficulties of being a colonial, for which I had been unprepared, was that half the time I had no idea of what people were talking about, and what the place-names signified. I had to feel my way like someone traversing a minefield. It was all right with big centres like Manchester, Liverpool and Glasgow, made familiar by schoolroom maps, depicting the things for which each city was renowned; there had been a boot next to Leicester, a knife beside Sheffield, a bit of lace by Nottingham, a loom for Leeds and a trawler off Grimsby. But when people talked of Wincanton, Barnstaple and Saxmundham, I did not know if these were neighbouring villages or Scottish castles or important towns; and whether you could get there on a bicycle or needed two days in a train.

There was also a mysterious language of numbers, spoken freely by Gertrude's young men. Eventually I realized that numbers such as fifth, ninth, tenth, sixteenth, twenty-first and sixtieth were the names of army regiments, though I never did sort out which were Lancers, Dragoons, Rifles or Hussars. Even then, confusion lay in wait; I thought the twelfth, for instance, was sure to be a regiment, but it turned out to be the day when people started to shoot grouse. The fourth was easier because it was generally linked with June, unless you were talking to an American, when it was in July. Phrases obscure to me but plain to everyone else kept on popping up, such as the Season, the Northern Meeting, the Enclosure and the Private View.

Not that these topics were part of normal Nathan's Orchard conversation, when there was any conversation; this was frequently suspended by my aunt's sulks. The names and numbers arose only when Gertrude came home with one of her young men. Gertrude did not bring young men home if she could avoid it, but as she received no allowance, and had no marketable skill, she often lacked the money to buy a railway ticket. Too proud to admit her poverty, and I suppose lacking in the self-confidence to laugh it off, she must have suffered agonies, and skated on a lot of thin ice. Unmarried girls were not expected to tip the butler, and could get away with half-crowns for the maids; but there was no dodging the cost of railway tickets. Fortunately, many of the young men Gertrude knew possessed motor cars.

On this occasion she turned up in a red sports car with a young man called Tony who was tall, fairish, with hair slightly receding, pale blue eyes, a small moustache and a rather smudgy kind of face. He had a dimple on his chin. Uncle Jack came to the door to meet them. A visitor had either to drive into the farmyard, which was full of mud, dung and scurrying piglets, or to leave his car by a wooden wicket gate, badly in need of paint, and follow a path equally in need of weeding through an overgrown garden to another door; we never quite knew which was the front and which the back of the house.

"My wife asked me to apologize, she's exercising the dogs," Uncle Jack explained. "I'll help you bring in your kit. Don't know what's happened to all our fellows; busy time, you know." The fellows, one was left to surmise—the footman, the butler and possibly an under gardener or so—were, in this informal, down-to-earth, lets-all-pull-together establishment, instead of cleaning the silver or tending the hot-houses, helping to stook the corn.

"The thing is," Gertrude remarked, "Tony's got a dog in the car."

"Hope you don't mind, sir. The thing is, I'm taking her on to the trials at Huntercombe."

"Her," my uncle said briefly, succumbing to what we called his rocking-horse look. "That's torn it."

"She wouldn't hurt a fly, honestly, sir. Never even puts up her hackles."

"Bitches fight bitches," said my uncle briefly, rolling back his forehead. "And they are all bitches in this house." Uncle Jack's tone was almost silky and he looked slightly sideways at Tony. It was believed that he had no sense of humour, but at times I was not sure.

"We can put her in a loose-box," Gertrude suggested. "It's only for a couple of nights. We can bribe Perce to keep it quiet."

Uncle Jack frowned, looking bonier than ever.

"Perce has his failings, but venery is not among them." I had no idea what venery meant, but it sounded like one of those vices which, while not actually nameless, could be read about in books that had been put into brown paper covers.

For a few alarming moments I found myself alone with Tony in the sitting room, which smelt of dog and the usual boiled tripe. Never introducing anyone, I had discovered, was another English custom, or at any rate a Nathan Orchard's one.

"Another sister, eh?" Tony inquired, fingering his incipient moustache.

"No, a cousin."

"Ah, cousin. Going to the Fulbrights' dance?"

"No."

"To Bill and Sally's for the twelfth?"

"No."

"Oh."

Silence fell, except for the grandfather clock. Tony made one more valiant effort.

"Fond of dogs, eh?"

"Yes. Well, some dogs."

"Chap I know's got one of those Salukis. Flat as a playing card, looks as if it had been run over by a steam roller."

"Perhaps it has?"

"Eh? Oh. Perhaps it has—ha-ha-ha! That's a good one. Ha-ha." He giggled mirthlessly, and I tried a sort of giggle too.

We were rescued by Uncle Jack, who took Tony to his study:

a dark, damp room—nearly all the rooms were dark and damp—across the hall and full of wall maps, tin uniform chests, books of extraordinary dullness and unpaid bills. The heads of half a dozen bare-fanged foxes, each on a wooden shield with a little plaque on which the circumstances of its demise were recorded, adorned the walls, together with several mottled prints of the Moonlight Steeplechase. The maps were stuck all over with pins with coloured heads that marked the progress of campaigns in the Peninsula War, of which my uncle was making a study; but recently he had got deflected on to Eastern Religions, a subject that had first come to his notice on the North-West Frontier, where he had had a great deal to do with mules.

Gertrude appeared from the tidying-up which an open sports car rendered necessary. Her skin was as soft and smooth as a magnolia petal. She wore long jade ear-rings, used a tortoise-shell cigarette-holder and had imitation pearls.

"Well, coz," she said, "you haven't changed."

As I had not been ten when she had last seen me, and was now eighteen, this could scarcely have been true. "That's a natty two-piece," she added, "I like the colour scheme. Beige is just the thing. I couldn't wear such a *big* check myself, but it suits you."

I knew from her tone of voice that it did not—I was too lumpy. "Nathan's Orchard doesn't seem to have changed either."

"Worse luck. Mummy's even more awful if anything. Lucky you, not having to stay here. But then of course you're clever. I could never have got into a college."

"You didn't try. It isn't difficult."

"That's just your modesty."

It was not; about all you had to do in those days was to fill in a form and pay the fees. Colleges and universities were short of students, not the other way round; O and A levels were still unborn. There was an examination, it was true, but it did not seem to matter how you did in it, except in the case of Oxford and Cambridge where you had to pass in Latin. This I was unable to do, since no one at the school I had attended for a year in Nairobi could teach it. So I was not going to Oxford or to Cambridge but to Reading. No one would believe it had a

university. It was known only for Huntley & Palmers' biscuits
and for Suttons' seeds; and possibly, among the intelligentsia,
for the association between its jail and Oscar Wilde.

"Ralph isn't clever, and he's at Oxford," I pointed out. Ralph
was another cousin, two years older than Gertrude.

"Oh, well, he's a man and he's rich. At least, he isn't really
rich but he pretends to be. He keeps two hunters at Magdalen.
Would you like to come to the Fulbrights' dance?"

"I haven't been asked."

"I think I could arrange it."

"I shouldn't know anyone."

Gertrude laughed a tinkling sort of laugh, the opposite of a
chuckle. "You'll have to break the ice sometime. Have you got
a frock?"

"A sort of one." Maggie had insisted on an evening dress at
Derry & Toms. It was very short, above the knee, and very
straight, bright green and with a v-neck and silver braid. I
could not repress a wish to wear it.

"I'll ring up Vera Fulbright," Gertrude promised. Nathan's
Orchard was not on the telephone, so that was an excuse to go
to Otterbourne in Tony's red car.

The return of Aunt Madge from the daily exercising ritual
was never unobtrusive. Suddenly the house became full of fox-
terriers snapping, frisking and scratching, and jumping with
muddy feet on to sofas and chairs which were covered with old
blankets in an ill-found hope of protecting loose covers; the
struggle had really been abandoned some years ago and everything was dirty, and apt to harbour fleas. "It's clean dirt," my
aunt would occasionally say. The fleas were supposed to be a
different kind from those that bit humans.

"There was an adder on Kingscliffe," she said, her heavy
boots clumping across the hall. Kingscliffe was the hill on which
the dogs were nearly always exercised.

Uncle Jack had emerged from his study with Tony. "I doubt
if anyone has seen an adder in this part of the country for a long
time."

"*I* saw one today."

"Are you quite sure it really was an adder, dearest?" Uncle
Jack was using his silkiest tone.

"Do you think I don't know an adder when I see one? It hissed at Mignonette and Madonna."

"Adders are easily confused with harmless grass-snakes."

"So you think it was a harmless grass-snake that nearly killed Mignonette and Madonna? I suppose if I'd been bitten by this viper and died in agony on Kingscliffe you'd have put it down to my imagination and said a harmless grass-snake——"

"I never *said* it was a harmless grass-snake, darling, only that it's easy to——"

"Of course it would have been a splendid thing if I *had* been bitten by an adder, and Kate too I expect, not to mention all the dogs, and then you would have been left in peace with your military studies——"

"Darling, Gertrude has arrived with a young man whose name I didn't catch, we had better——"

"Released from the bondage of family life you could have had the adder stuffed and put into a glass case like that fish or those unfortunate capercailzie, or you could have turned it into a divinity like one of those disgusting Hindu creatures with dozens of arms and legs, it's a pity that——"

"Gertrude is here with a young man!" Uncle Jack shouted. His skin was getting ominously mottled and his moustache bristling like the hackles of a dog.

"Kate drove off the adder with a hunting crop, it was a mistake I can see now, we should have let the adder do its worst and then you——"

"GERTRUDE HAS COME WITH A YOUNG MAN!"

"Gertrude and the young man could have had the place to themselves and entertained Vera Fulbright to afternoon tea in a civilized manner and taken the blankets off the chairs and talked about Tutankhamen's tomb, though whether Nellie—— where is this young man you go on about? Madonna, come off that chair, you know it's Honeysuckle's, and Dogrose, *will* you leave Violet alone?"

Dogrose and Violet were engaged in amorous byplay and poor Tony was standing in the doorway, pink in the face and with his dimpled jaw dropping, like a rock lashed by a confusion of waves. Responding, perhaps, to the emotional climate, Dogrose and Madonna, after a short overture of growls, set upon each other, and a great deal of whip-cracking, shouting and barking followed; by the time it was over, Tony had vanished with Gertrude in the red car, Uncle Jack had withdrawn with mottled face and flashing eyes and empty threats into his study, Nellie had arrived with a bucket of water and Kate and I had edged our way out of sight, and then into the orchard, where there was a blackbird singing, out of season, in a hollow tree.

"There was an owl nesting in that tree last year," Kate remarked. "Do you remember when we found a robin's nest in a chest of drawers in that old shed? It's fallen down now. The shed I mean."

"We used it as a kind of house, and gave a tea party for the Cholmondely-Chetwynds, do you remember?"

"Dressed up in mummy's tea-gowns and things."

We had been great ones for dressing up in those days; a big oak chest in the attic had disgorged everything from velvet tea-gowns of Edwardian vintage to Uncle Jack's spurs, and a party hat that had once supported a stuffed parrot, and painted fans, and a moth-eaten pair of silk court knee-breeches, and several old milking smocks, and a sporran.

"Do you remember nanny as one of the Princes in the Tower?" As she must have weighed at least fifteen stone and her face was wrinkled as a walnut shell, the sight had been memorable; osprey feathers had nodded in a velvet tam-o-shanter and she had sung inappropriate ditties in an Irish voice, her breath smelling of brandy.

"And the Eternal Triangle."

We had been fond of plays, and had made them up ourselves as a rule; but for this one, we had used the plot of a story in one of the magazines in the w.c., because it had the right number of characters—three; nanny took part only as an extra, a butler perhaps, or a railway porter, or a policeman if there was a murder in it, as there often was, and Joanna was too young to participate. Gertrude always had to be the heroine; she refused to play male parts, and took so long to array herself and put on make-up that we used to grow impatient, and started without her once or twice. On this occasion I was the husband who returned from the Front in uniform—there was plenty of that

in the box, including an enormous revolver—to find his wife
in the arms of a lover, who of course was Kate, enveloped in an
old dinner jacket with her hair screwed up under a sombrero.
"Unhand my wife!" I cried. The guilty pair sprang apart,
Gertrude flung her arms round my neck as, brandishing the
revolver, I pursued Kate, in turn clutching her sombrero with
one hand and her trousers with the other, round the end of the
room set apart as a stage. Her exit was confused by an inevitable
fall, swathed in trouser, while I wrestled with the revolver,
which had stuck in its holster, and retreated to the sofa to clasp
my head in my hands. "To think that it should have come to
this! While I am fighting for my King and Country you have
betrayed me with this dago. Deeply as it grieves me to say it,
you are a strumpet, nothing less!" At this point Uncle Jack
had risen majestically from his chair, moustache a-bristle,
proclaiming in his parade-ground voice: "I will not listen to
balderdash from foul-mouthed little girls who ought to be in
bed—why didn't you have them taught the piano?" The performance had ended rather lamely after that, with only three
left in the audience— Aunt Madge, Nellie and Perce, who had
come in with news of a sick cow.

Aunt Madge had been rather amused, and given one of her
chuckles. "Wherever did you pick up that word?"

"It's in the magazine," Gertrude said.

"What's wrong with a strumpet?" Kate inquired. She was
then only about eight or nine.

"They're not respectable," Aunt Madge explained.

"They're good with butter."

"*Buttered* strumpets?"

"For tea."

"Oh, I see. You're too young for plays about love. Next time
you'd better stick to Dracula or Back of The North Wind."

"I'm tired of goblins."

"Bulldog Drummond, then."

It all seemed a long time ago. I wondered what had happened
to the dressing-up things in the chest. Kate said:

"The moth got in so badly they were burnt after nanny died.
Her room was stacked with empty bottles, she must have been
practically pickled like one of those snakes in a jar in a lab."

"I wonder where she got the money."

"She put it down to our account at Hodges' mostly. Daddy made a frightful stink when he found out."

"I should have thought Aunt Madge must have known."

"I'm sure she did."

As was to be expected, the business of the adder sent Aunt Madge into one of her sulks. At one period we used to time these, and the record was a day short of three weeks. In theory, we ignored them, but this was like trying to ignore a bad smell in the room, even a corpse. Aunt Madge would talk to the dogs, but every human advance met a blank wall. Meals were the worst, because at the best of times she sat at the table for what seemed like hours and hours, after everyone had finished eating, —just sat, we never knew why. Conversation dried up, and time stretched out like chewing gum; the silence almost suffocated you. You wanted to scream, or anyway I did. This was no doubt Aunt Madge's intention. It was a sort of contest, a battle of wills. To have got you to scream or fly hysterically from the room or burst into abuse would have been set and match to her. I never could understand why we all went on sitting in that dreary room, with its high windows and brown damp-stained walls, instead of simply getting up and walking out. There was some kind of mental blackmail, almost hypnotism, going on.

"A fit of the sulks," as Uncle Jack called it, was bad enough when the family was on its own, but when there was a guest it was excruciating. Gertrude invented all sorts of excuses to discourage the young men who gave her lifts from staying overnight, but as, in the world in which she lived—or rather penetrated intermittently like a bee foraging in a flower bed—it was taken for granted that people stayed with each other, she was not always successful. She had failed with Tony, who had come for two nights. He seemed to have a lot of luggage, and Gertrude had to carry off as best as she could a warning that not only would his evening clothes not be laid out on his bed, but that no one at Nathan's Orchard changed for dinner. He was a nice young man, and tried to look understanding.

"Bohemian, eh? Your family."

"Well, daddy . . ."

"Writing a book," Tony firmly stated. "Told me so himself. About the Seventh."

To explain away Aunt Madge's sulks was harder, in fact impossible. Uncle Jack did his best by talking a great deal about his regiment, and his experiences on the North-West Frontier, Ashanti and in other parts of the globe. These were of but slender interest to Tony, whose eyes turned continually to Gertrude with the look of a conscientious gundog puzzled by some baffling odour or confused instruction from its master. His first attempt to start a conversation with his hostess was totally ignored, his second elicited a muted grunt which might have resulted from a touch of wind; after that, he gave up trying. But you could not ignore Aunt Madge; her silence had a tangible quality, it permeated the whole room, together with the usual smell of tripe simmering in the kitchen. A young girl called Lily, a niece of Perce's, stumped round the room in a work-stained apron, breathing heavily, to thrust in front of us portions of boiled mutton, soggy cabbage and over-cooked potatoes, take the plates away and in due course bring coffee, which was surprisingly good. Uncle Jack was a connoisseur of coffee, or at least wanted it to be drinkable, and had persevered with Nellie until she had grasped the simple technique that had been followed in the officers' mess at Poona. Over the coffee he and Tony discussed prospects for the twelfth, which led on to tales of shikari in Kashmir. Even these flagged after a while, and at about half-past two, when Tony's fidgeting was giving ground for alarm, Uncle Jack said in his silkiest tones:

"Shall we adjourn, dearest, to the drawing-room?"

Aunt Madge continued to stare at a vase of mecanopsis in the centre of the table, a dog on her knee and a cigarette between her fingers. Uncle Jack cleared his throat.

"I think, dear, our guest would like to make a move. He has some business, I understand, to see to this afternoon in Otterbourne."

I was sorry for Gertrude, although she did not herself do much to help. Perhaps there was nothing much she could do. "All Gertrude ever does is look pale and interesting," Aunt Madge sometimes remarked. "Pale, anyway. Constipation rather than intellect." Interesting or not, she looked beautiful.

Now and again she caught Tony's eye and gave a strained half-smile. Kate hummed under her breath, gave her mutton to the dogs and, when the silence had become as clinging as a thick fog, came out now and again with a remark that provided its own full-stop, such as: "Have persimmons come in season yet?" "Is it true that whales blubber because their epiglottis is constricted?"

Somehow or other, our release from the dining room did eventually occur, and it was not surprising that Gertrude and her current young man, having escaped by car, often failed to turn up for supper. In the absence of a telephone there was no way to notify Aunt Madge, who would abuse the ill manners of the young, while Uncle Jack invariably sat up in his study until they returned. Then he would usher them in with an icy politeness calculated to kill stone-dead any spirit of jollity that might have been generated by dinner at the Sheldrake Arms or a visit to the local, bolt and bar the door and wish them a frosty goodnight.

And yet, despite all this, my aunt and uncle had their amiable side. Gertrude, in her teens, had befriended an unprepossessing fellow-schoolgirl, with spectacles and teeth in braces and thick serge dresses, whose parents were in India, and invited her to stay one Christmas holidays. As a guest this girl, inappropriately named Maybud, had been anything but congenial; she was terrified of animals, sat about and did nothing, laid down the law, picked her nose and failed to switch off lights on landings; nevertheless my aunt suffered her if not gladly at least resignedly, persuaded her to read instead of mooning, taught her to knit and invited her again, so that she made a second home at Nathan's Orchard.

Then there was the incident of the wayward pullets. After a lot of doubt, hesitation and negotiation, old Sullivan bought a dozen pullets, intending to sell eggs to Mr. Hodge who kept a general store in Otterbourne. In due course they were penned in the orchard and provided with a house complete with nesting boxes. They were said to be in full lay when they arrived. Every day, and several times a day, treading on the sides of her feet to spare the bunions, old nanny waddled down to collect her booty; but the pullets went on strike, and every day the nesting boxes were dismally empty. Hope sprang

eternal in her wheezing breast, only to be cruelly dashed again
and again. The strain began to tell, and she was found in tears
in the nursery. "I expect they've stolen a nest in the orchard,"
Aunt Madge said. Sullivan replied that this was impossible, the
wire of the pen was firmly pegged; just to make sure, several
times we searched the orchard.

This went on until one day my aunt, beaming and chuckling,
summoned Sullivan to the foot of an apple tree beside the pond.
Covered by grass, a large clutch of eggs lay hidden in a hollow.
"What did I tell you?" said Aunt Madge. "They stole the nest."
Sullivan clucked unbelievingly, but could not dispute the evidence, especially when a hole underneath the wire was discovered, large enough for a pullet to squeeze through. "Let it
be," Perce advised. "They'm used to it." She took his advice,
and every morning found two or three eggs under the apple
tree. One morning, going out early, I caught Perce taking a
couple of eggs from his pocket and slipping them into the nest.
He grinned, and said: "Orders from the missus. Bit of a joke,
like." It was not a joke really, but an act of compassion. Eventually the pullets began to lay again, and did so in the proper
place; and no more eggs were discovered in the hollow under
the tree.

Although my aunt was often grumpy, unkind or silent, now
and again she made a remark that stuck in my mind because it
was perceptive or sensible. Once, when I was running down a
book, she said: "I've never read a book yet I haven't got something out of, even the worst has something to offer." Also she
remarked, when we were starting for a picnic in a hailstorm,
"In this country, one should never put anything off because of
the weather."

Chapter Three

Gertrude succeeded in getting me invited to the Fulbrights'
house-party. It was perhaps typical of the cautious attitude
to life we had all adopted that it never occurred to me that she
might have done this simply because she thought I would enjoy
the party and wanted to promote my enjoyment; we both knew
that I should be miserable. I thought her motive was partly to
make a fool of me, and partly because she hoped to offload on
to me a dull young man she was bored with, leaving her free to
concentrate on Tony. Aunt Madge deplored the whole under-
taking.

"A lot of damned nonsense," she sniffed. "Girls who should
know better got up like tarts with skirts above their hideous
knock-knees, jumping about like a lot of epileptic apes, and
then those long-haired creatures, you couldn't call them men,
working themselves into hysterical frenzies with those ghastly
instruments."

"Instruments?" Uncle Jack inquired suspiciously.

"Invented by niggers. I can't think how Vera Fulbright can
bring herself to allow it at Montleven, with George Fulbright
in his position."

This was the age of the Charleston, the Black Bottom and the
Blues. There was the young Duke Ellington and the husky-
voiced, dusky-complexioned Hutch who sent tremors up and
down the spines of adolescents. Kate adored Hutch, but I was
in thrall to Jack Smith, the Whispering Baritone. We had an
ancient gramophone so worn-out you had to crank the handle
several times in the course of a single record, and some cracked
old discs, and had to stuff a duster, or pair of knickers, into the
hole from which the sound emerged, whenever we heard Aunt
Madge clumping about downstairs and boiling up the tripe.

Kate and I were practising the Charleston and had to retreat
to the attic, bare-boarded now and full of dust and spiders, to
perform the curious slithering motion of the feet that made the
floors shake and dust tickle our nostrils. This kind of dance has,

ever since, been linked for me with the smell of dust and bare boards and with a clandestine feeling; even the attic was safe only when Aunt Madge was on the farm with Perce or exercising the terriers. Sometimes shafts of sunlight would strike through panes of dirty glass to illuminate thousands, probably millions, of motes dancing their own golden Charleston, as our stockinged feet scraped and thumped against the boards, perhaps disturbing the ghosts of Nellie's illegitimate and incestuous babies.

Montleven was a very large house with a moat, a park containing deer, enormous oaks and mottled sheep, and with several brick-walled gardens. Inside its turreted walls it had a hall with cutlasses, and a minstrels' gallery; long corridors lined by glass-fronted cases containing mysterious objects known as bric-à-brac; dull portraits in huge gold frames, and leather-bound books no one ever opened. Parts of it were very old, and parts had been added in the nineteenth century. These included a dining room with a vaulted mock-Italian ceiling, a big bay window, and enormous radiators as thick as the hulls of battleships—central heating was something very bold and new and was considered dangerously effete by most of the County. The Fulbrights tended to be apologetic about this lapse on the part of the fourteenth Viscount who had installed it about the time of the Boer War. We understood that, what with the radiators and the hot-houses, Montleven ate a ton of coal a day.

The house-party was even more alarming than I had anticipated. Everyone knew each other, no one knew me, and they naturally ignored my existence. For this I was thankful, but it gave me a curiously disembodied feeling, and at times I began to doubt my own existence; perhaps I had died without knowing it, like characters in the play *Outward Bound*. Also I lived in terror of failing to observe some piece of ritual—being late for dinner, or early for breakfast, or using a knife with a soufflé, or a spoon for pudding that called for a fork.

Most intimidating of all were the servants. They were more like robots than people. I was not used to servants, at least to white ones; the Africans of our household had been bursting at the seams with a life of their own. They had laughed, shouted to each other and chatted; the kitchen was always packed with visitors and children, and at night we could hear singing and drumming near their huts, and smell their cooking fires. If anyone was ill, he would come clasping his stomach and rolling his eyes and crying: "Give me medicine, strong medicine quickly or I shall die!" It was quite impossible to imagine any such approach by the Fulbrights' butler, a figure as stately as a stuffed ambassador, or any of the footmen in maroon livery coats, or by the maids who seemed to have no hearts or even voices, but stiff, masked faces.

I was unnerved from the moment when a footman asked me for my keys. "Keys of what?" "Your suitcase, miss." I had never locked a suitcase in my life, and realized with a sinking stomach that someone else was going to unpack. Mine were not possessions that could stand up to the scrutiny of Montleven maids. I had no silver-backed brushes, no cut-glass bottles, no dressing-case even, and my underclothes were made, I think, of lock-knit rayon, or something like that, held up by strong elastic; none of the flimsy, lace-edged creations in which *crêpe-de-chine* and a material called triple *ninon* were involved. In those days rich people had their underclothes hand-made by some little woman —they seemed always to be little—in a village, or off the Fulham Road. Even my green satin dress with silver braid from Derry & Toms lost its pride and spendour. I would have given all I possessed, such as it was, to go back to Nathan's Orchard or, better still, to Africa.

There was a writing desk in my room—a room with a large four-poster bed, heavy brocade curtains and enough cupboard space for several families—and I started a letter to my mother. Disturbed by the booming of a gong, I left it half-done with the pen by its side. When I returned, the ornate silver blotter had been straightened, a new piece of blotting paper inserted and a fresh nib put into the penholder. This intimidated me more than anything else. I felt myself to be hemmed in by an army of invisible, soundless goblins who watched my every movement from a mysterious recess, and from whom I could never escape, even in the lavatory. Could the rich really like this kind of life, I wondered? Evidently they did, and some of the poor, like Gertrude, envied it.

My host shared the unreality of his servants, and might have
been cut out of cardboard. He was good-looking in a chiselled
sort of way, with a short straight nose and a thick moustache,
and was quiet in manner, unobtrusive and polite; he "did things
in the County", whatever that meant; perhaps that he had been,
or was, the Lord Lieutenant. He was over-shadowed by his wife,
considerably the younger, whose grandfather had made a fortune and espoused the daughter of a poor but genuine peer. She
had hoped to marry her daughter Vera to a future Prime
Minister or, at the least, a titled Foreign Secretary, but had
nailed her colours to the wrong party and was obliged to be
content with George Fulbright, who was at any rate a fifteenth
Viscount, if not a man of mark. She secured for him the
Governorship of one of the Australian States, but this was not a
success, and the outbreak of war enabled him to hurry back to
his territorial regiment, win several medals and finally return
to his broad acres, his hunting and his County activities, only
partially impeded by weak lungs due to poison gas.

This was an awkward season when nothing could be chased,
killed or competed for; Cowes week was over, the twelfth yet
to come. There was a puppy show, where large, rumbunctious
canines with names like Challenger and Thunderer bounded
about a ring, and there was a belated local agricultural show.
Otherwise the guests cleared undergrowth in the woods, made
bonfires, collected beechmast for the pigs, played tennis if it
was not raining and squash if it was, repaired to a nearby golf-
course, or went out hacking—on horses, not at trees. The first
necessity was to be healthily employed out of doors.

Gertrude produced a nondescript, sandy-haired young man,
looking as if he needed a course of good square meals, and said:

"This is Jumbo Matheson. He's in the Navy and looks
ripping in his uniform, it's so attractive, isn't it? Jumbo's been
to all sorts of exciting places so you'll have plenty to talk
about."

On this alarming note she left us, having Tony in tow, both
in white tennis clothes and looking handsome enough for a
musical comedy. Jumbo's pale, protruding eyes followed them
and had, all too understandably, no interest in me. I was wearing the brown and beige check in which I had lost confidence

ever since Gertrude had commented on the size of the checks. Everyone else was in skirts and jumpers—well-cut, light, non-creasable tweeds with small, discreet patterns like herring-bone, worn with soft, fluffy woollens that were either too new to need washing, or had been washed in special ways by expert maids so as to preserve their elasticity.

The fact that Jumbo Matheson was in the Navy partially made up for his nondescript appearance. During the war I had pasted into an exercise book photographs of ships and members of their crews that had reached us in *The Illustrated London News*, together with anything else of a Naval nature that came my way, and in history it was accounts of victories at sea rather than on land that had excited me. Why this nautical bias had arisen I have no idea. I had scarcely ever met a sailor and there were none, so far as I knew, in our family—perhaps this *was* the reason, they had the attraction of the unknown, plus the uniform. Anyway, here was a real sailor at last.

"What ship are you in?" I inquired.

Jumbo Matheson made a conscious effort to focus his attention. He was called Jumbo, of course, because he was so weedy, just as huge beefy men were always Tiny. He replied that *Periwinkle* was the name of his ship. This was a vessel I had never heard of. I had hoped that he might say H.M.S. *Renown* or *Repulse*. He added, rather apologetically, "She's a mine-sweeper."

"Oh." Minesweepers were necessary of course, and in war-time their crews were very brave, but they did lack glamour. He added:

"Do you know Miss Gilbert well?"

"Gertrude? She's my cousin."

"Oh!" He looked at me for the first time. "That must . . . She's very . . . I've only met her twice before. Though I think we were at one or two children's parties."

"You live somewhere near?"

"At South Molton." I had no idea whether that was a mile away or near John o' Groats. "I'm not there much."

"I suppose not."

Conversation languished; it was mid-afternoon, looked like rain, and somehow we had both escaped, or drifted away from,

the organized activities of the house-party. It would be a long
time before the gong summoned us to tea. A gusty wind blew.
We walked along a gravel path with edges trimmed as neatly
as a finger-nail, amid shrubs and trees so groomed and spaced
as to allow frequent glimpses of a reed-fringed lake with
water-lilies and swans. The path, the silence, the afternoon
seemed to have no end. At last Jumbo Matheson cleared his
throat, hesitated, cleared it again, took out a handkerchief, blew
his nose and flapped his hand at a fly.

"Midges bad this year."

"Yes, I suppose they are."

Something was clearly weighing on his mind, something he
wanted to say but could not, as if he had oral constipation. At
last it came out.

"I don't hunt."

"No, I suppose not. Not in a minesweeper."

"That's the snag about the Navy. Besides, my father's dead."

"Oh. I'm sorry . . . Mine's in Africa."

"Oh, yes?" I had already learnt that a reference to Africa
was a conversation-stopping, not a conversation-opening,
remark. At first I had naïvely supposed that people would be
eager to hear about Africa and its wonders, and even if they
did not hang upon my words, at least that they would occasionally listen. This was very far from being the case. To them,
Africa was a remote, uninteresting region to which now and
again a young man in one of the numerical regiments might
repair to shoot animals, possibly because he had met with an
amorous misfortune or, more frequently, got too heavily into
debt. When he reappeared he was not expected to bore people
with accounts of his experiences among lions and savages.
However, in this case, the information did start off a train of
thought.

"Then perhaps you don't hunt either?"

"No." Being, at that time, a stickler for accuracy, I added:
"We did hunt sometimes when we lived at Thika. Mainly
jackals or duikers. Occasionally a warthog or a porcupine."

"Well, no porcupines here. I wonder if Miss Gilbert . . ."

"It seems funny to hear her called that."

"Miss Gilbert . . . Gertrude of course . . . A lovely name."

"Gert doesn't think so."

"I wonder if she'd like to see . . . But I don't suppose she'd be interested in *Periwinkle*. Though she does belong to one of the new Flora class."

I had always longed to see a real naval vessel flying the White Ensign, even a minesweeper would have done; now it was Gertrude who was being offered an opportunity she certainly would not appreciate.

"Where is she?" I inquired. "I mean *Periwinkle*."

"Down at Pompey."

"Have you got a car?"

"Well, no."

After its brief spurt, the conversation sputtered out. When tea was over, the rain was thought to have cleared off, and we were marshalled to the tennis courts, all in white. For tennis, though not at any other time, legs might be bare. Gertrude's, I noticed, were smooth and hairless, unlike mine, which to my dismay were revealed to be unfashionably hirsute. Did she, then, shave her legs as well as her armpits? Or use one of those preparations advertised for removing superfluous hair? Luckily my hairs were fair and not bristly, but they were ineluctably there.

Of the dance itself I can remember little, no doubt because I hated it and therefore my mind more or less expunged it from the record. It was, of course, a very splendid affair. Banks and banks of massed flowers filled the hall, liveried men in white gloves seemed everywhere, huge chandeliers sparkled like ice crystals, there were two London bands, white ties and tails made the men looked distinguished, even the sloppy, dumpy ones. There were bridge rooms for the elderly, an enormous supper at long tables in the dining room, plenty of sitting-out rooms with subdued lights and more flowers, masses of champagne and a kind of iced cup. We had programmes with little pencils attached. Lady Fulbright and several of her minions went round prodding the unattached young men into asking girls to dance. The supper dance I had with Jumbo, who was very glum; he had managed to get his name on to Gertrude's programme for one dance only, and then she had cut it in favour of Tony.

"All the same," Jumbo said morosely, "I wouldn't be in his shoes."

"I should have thought . . ."

"Bad blood."

This was quite a new idea about Tony. "Madness in the family?"

"Oh, everything. His grandfather died of drink I believe. His father gambled everything away, or would have if he hadn't married a rich American in time to save the property. They say his mother drugs."

"You wouldn't think all that to look at him."

"It comes out in the end."

I could not see him at the moment, nor Gertrude either; probably they were sitting out. I hoped so, but I had noticed him dancing several times with a dark, well-dressed girl of a vaguely exotic appearance; she looked as if she was a light, supple, imaginative dancer, and had a presence, a manner—she might have been on the stage. She was altogether more sophisticated than Gertrude.

At last it was over, and we could go to bed. Thankfully, I made my way up the wide, polished stairs beneath portraits of previous Viscounts in ermines, vowing that I would never go to any more country-house dances. It was, of course, extremely unlikely that I should ever be asked. Our bedrooms opened off a long corridor, like stables of a fabulously handsome kind. Everything inside was dark and hushed—deep-piled carpets, heavy brocade curtains, even the wallpaper had a velvety pile. It was like being in a sort of cocoon. From years of living in the tropics, I had formed the habit of walking barefoot with my toes turned up to avoid picking up jiggas. I went on doing this for years, and reflected how absurd it was; a jigga at Montleven was about as likely as a belly-dancer in the Vatican.

I was not sleepy, and when I had undressed, thought I would say goodnight to Gertrude and find out how she got the hairs off her legs. I knocked, there was a pause, and then a sharp "Who's there?" "It's only me." "Oh, you. All right, come in."

Gertrude was standing by the dressing table, not looking pleased; her long jade ear-rings quivered and seemed to express

distrust, like a cat's whiskers when they stiffen and spread.
Tony was sprawled in an arm-chair smoking a cigar and looking
flushed and self-satisfied; he did not bother to get to his feet.

"What is it, coz?" Gertrude's voice was not at all cosy.

"I'm sorry, I didn't mean to barge in. I just wanted to say
goodnight."

"What is there to be sorry for?" she inquired sharply. "I
hope you enjoyed yourself. I saw you getting on with Jumbo
like a house on fire."

Sometimes Gertrude's patronizing tone could be irritating.
"Who was that attractive dark girl Tony was dancing with?"
I inquired.

"Ah, Ruth." Tony did not exactly snigger, but his voice had a
knowing inflection. Gertrude said smoothly, "Jewish, of
course."

"Related to the Sassoons," Tony said.

"Dear Tony, you believe everything people tell you. Still,
I wish her luck. Messing about with that old bottom-pincher
three times her age! You watch out, coz."

"Watch out for what?"

"Our host, silly." Gertrude spoke in tones of long-suffering
patience. "Famous bottom-pincher among other things. If he
offers to teach you to skate, watch your step."

"Why should he teach me to skate?"

"Oh, don't be so thick. Well, see you in the morning."

Even a goodnight call upon a cousin, if of the same sex,
was, I now realized, a *gaffe* at Montleven; even the fine linen
sheets had a slithery, unwelcoming coldness; a ghost might all
too easily step down from one of the picture-frames, the contempt an invisible housemaid must have felt when she laid out
my cheap rayon night-dress seemed to linger on the air like a
bad smell. A jigga, however itchy, would have been an old
friend.

People drifted in for breakfast, and everyone went on eating
or peeling a peach and did not get up. The sideboard was lined
with dishes in heavy silver covers sitting on a long hot-plate,
and it was interesting to lift each cover in turn and see what it
concealed. There were eggs scrambled, poached, fried and
boiled; lots of crisp bacon in very thin rashers; sausages lying

snugly side by side like piglets sleeping off a suckling orgy; kidneys on toast; and fish of various kinds—haddock, kedgeree and kippers; certain fish were correct at breakfast but not later in the day, whereas species like trout, sole and turbot could be eaten from lunch-time onwards, but not before. All this came after lashings of porridge. How could so much be stowed away, even by a score of eaters? The preparations must have taken hours. Every slice of toast was trimmed, and crisp without being too frangible. There were also rolls, and three kinds of marmalade, and honey in the comb, and masses of fruit. No wonder tradition demanded that breakfast should be eaten in silence. There was simply no time to talk.

I sidled into a place as far away as I could get from the head of the table where our host sat behind *The Times*. Beside him sat the dark girl Ruth, inhaling fumes of coffee from a big, thin cup as if it had been old brandy. She had the kind of creamy skin I envied, and thick hair fashionably short, almost an Eton crop, and an even more enviable calm and poise; things went on around her and she did not mind or notice; as an emerald or a ruby holds the light, she held attention without making any apparent effort to attract it. Her surname was French.

Tony came in and helped himself to kippers, eggs and kidneys all together and sat down next to her. I found I was beside Jumbo, who had finished his meal; his eyes looked more bulging and watery than ever.

"I don't suppose it would be the thing to smoke a pipe," he remarked. "Do you play golf?"

"I've tried, but I'm no good at it."

"Nor me. Played a bit in Aden."

"It must have been hot."

"Awfully. So it was in Singapore, but moister."

"Yes."

Silence at breakfast, I began to realize, was a good idea, but when you had finished eating, the ban ceased to apply. Jumbo soon tackled his favourite theme.

"How's your cousin this morning?"

"All right I expect."

"Does she play golf do you suppose?"

"I doubt it."

"Yes, I should think it was rather on the masculine side for her. She's too, somehow, well, delicate, in a way, I should think, for outdoor games. Chinese women never play them."

"I suppose not. But then she's not Chinese."

"Oh, no. Definitely not Chinese."

Vera Fulbright made an entrance; she had already consumed her breakfast, and gone out to get the day's activities in train.

"I'll just swallow another cup of coffee. I've telephoned for caddies and they're booked for ten thirty so the golfers must bestir themselves. The squash court's available, and there's plenty to be done in the shrubbery; Townsend has a good supply of spare macs. Now who's for golf?" She had a little pad and gold pencil and gave me an uneasy feeling of encirclement. Could I sneak off and read a book in my room? It seemed unlikely. George Fulbright, however, no doubt from long practice, knew how to go his own way.

"I am taking our charming guest Ruth to skate in Barnstaple, my dear," he announced.

"What a splendid idea! So few people are able to skate, and you are so fond of it. It exercises all the muscles, I believe."

She rang the bell. "Townsend, the small Daimler at eleven for his lordship, the Rolls at ten-thirty for the golfers, and if it clears up we'll want the Chrysler later, and tell Sparrow to send the horses round at eleven, please."

The hall at Montleven held a row of lockers, each bearing the name of a guest, in which we kept our coats and various accoutrements like tennis racquets, golf clubs, fishing rods, riding boots and so on. Mine, which had nothing in it but a macintosh, was next to Gertrude's, and here our paths crossed. She was in a riding habit. Although I had seen them in photographs, I had never actually seen a riding habit in the flesh, or rather cloth, before. It seemed to me strange that, to ride horses, women should dress up very much like nuns, in uniforms that bore the same names.

"Is anything wrong?" Gertrude asked, trying to inspect her own rear.

"Aren't all those skirts and things awfully heavy?"

"You do make such *odd* remarks. Have you seen Tony anywhere?"

"I think he's in the library."

"That doesn't sound at all like Tony. Who's he with?" Gertrude's voice had an edge to it, and she did not look rested. The approach of Jumbo, gazing at her like a faithful dog hoping to be patted, did not raise her spirits.

"It's going to clear up later, I think," he remarked. "If you don't my saying so, you do look ripping . . . I wish . . . Lady Fulbright put me down for golf. Everyone thinks sailors can't ride but in Malta . . ."

"You should have hoisted the signal of revolt, old man."

Tony had emerged from the library with Ruth, who was dressed for skating in a short, pleated navy skirt and a scarlet open-necked blouse which showed to the best advantage her excellent figure. Rink-attire seemed to me a great deal more becoming than horse-attire; but as rink skating took place indoors, it could rank only as a second-grade occupation, not to be taken quite seriously.

"Jumbo's far too polite to be a rebel, aren't you, Jumbo dear?" Gertrude smiled at Jumbo so warmly that he looked as if he had been hit by some powerful and invisible ray; he swallowed several times and one could almost feel him breaking into a gentle sweat under the armpits.

"Half the morning will be gone if we go on like this," she added. "Are you coming, Tony? Or have you found superior attractions in the library?"

"Of course I'm coming," Tony said crossly. "Which horses have they sent round? I'm not having the one that stumbles all over the place, a chestnut, I forget its name. There's a grey I wouldn't mind."

"Leaving the one that stumbles for me?"

"The grey's too wild for you, anyway. Well, come along then. So long, Ruth, see you later. I must learn to skate one of these days."

The golf was even worse than I had feared. The turf was soggy, and once off the fairway—my ball was almost always off the fairway—the grass was long and wet, bunkers devilishly placed, and my putting even wilder than usual. The caddy sized me up immediately and made no effort to conceal his scorn. I was partnered by Jumbo, and felt bitterly ashamed of the way I continually let him down. Our opponents were not much good either, but thanks to me they walked away with the game. Not that I minded; but to strive for victory and deplore defeat was clearly part of the Montleven tradition. Even after dinner, we went on playing games. There was billiards and snooker, *vingt-et-un* and bridge; if anyone was left over, or tried to edge away, he was quickly paired off with some other fugitive at a chess, backgammon or Chinese checkers' board.

On our final evening we had charades, which became hilarious and vulgar; jokes, words and innuendos that would have been banned in conversation were permitted at charades. Vera Fulbright set the tone by laughing at the childish jokes and covering her ears with her hands in mock embarrassment at the coarser ones. Our host had withdrawn to his study to work, he gave us to understand, on a speech for the House of Lords. This was doubted; he had put in, it was said, only two appearances in the Upper Chamber, one to oppose a bill extending workmen's compensation to gamekeepers, the other to prohibit the docking of horses' tails. He and Ruth had enjoyed a most successful day, we gathered, in the rink, punctuated by a fish-and-chip luncheon at an A.B.C.

Around midnight, nightcaps appeared, and so did Lord Fulbright. Ruth had vanished; so had Tony, I observed. Gertrude, pleading a headache, had gone to bed—alone this time, I surmised. The previous night had evidently not been a success; whether because she had gone too far, not far enough, or in the wrong direction, I longed to know, but never should. Perhaps it was all for the best, in view of Tony's bad blood.

I was flattered when our host came over to engage me in conversation in his gentle, half-abstracted, half-pedantic way.

"Let me see, it is South Africa you come from, is it not? Perhaps you ran across the de Crespignys there?"

"I'm afraid not. Actually it was East Africa, not South."

"Then probably you met the Bosanquets. He governed something out there I think. His wife was bitten by a camel, I remember, in a most unfortunate place. Or could it have been by a cannibal? I cannot exactly recall. Do you do much skating in South Africa?"

"East. I'm afraid not."

"There is no more useful accomplishment. It develops a sense of balance, which is so important for a girl. I should be delighted to arrange some lessons, if you would care to try."

"It's very kind of you, Lord Fulbright, but I——"

"I'm sure you will not regret it. You will need some boots, of course. The best place to get them is from a little bootmaker not far from Tattersall's; it would give me great pleasure to take you there. Shall we say next Wednesday at twelve o'clock? Afterwards we might enjoy a little luncheon; there is an excellent A.B.C. quite close at hand. I am very fond of A.B.C.'s; I consider they have the best fish and chips in London. Here we have a most expensive cook, but she cannot do chips as well as the A.B.C."

"It's very kind of you, Lord Fulbright, but——"

"That's settled, then. Now, if you will forgive me, I must see my other guests safely off to bed." He took my hand and lifted it to his lips in the best continental fashion. As he turned, there was no mistaking it; I felt a sharp nip on the left buttock. Then he was gone.

Nathan's Orchard was the same as ever, only more so; tripe was boiling, Nellie rolling out suet pastry, Uncle Jack lurking in his study, and Mignonette was having puppies by a half-retriever on Aunt Madge's bed. Tony declined an invitation to stay to lunch. Gertrude retired to her room with a headache, and did not emerge until tea-time; she looked pale and washed-out and I felt sure she had been crying. She snapped my head off when I tried to be nice.

"Anyone who brings a young man here's a lunatic," Kate observed.

"I suppose Gertie can't *make* them stay away."

"I should say the cook had typhoid, the cows foot-and-mouth, the dogs rabies and there was a suspected case of leprosy in the village."

"You'd get a lot of press reporters."

"Well, then, that both of my parents went down in the *Titanic*, I was brought up by an uncle who's in a lunatic asylum, my only other relative was Colonel Fawcett who disappeared in South America and I'm camping out with gypsies on Flamborough Head."

Chapter Four

THE time came for me to take my place at Reading. I had not expected dreaming spires exactly, or ancient quads, or even venerable dons sunk in meditation and gay young bloods breakfasting at noon off game pie and brandy; nevertheless so deeply was the Oxford image implanted on the mind, especially upon that of a colonial, that I looked at least for an architectural heart, for halls of dignity, an aroma of learning. And Reading, as I had observed from the map, like Oxford, stood upon the Thames; surely a river so traversed by history and romance, so ancient and so richly celebrated, would entwine itself about the university and make its presence felt.

London Road was not as squalid as many of the neighbouring streets consisting of squashed-together little dwellings dark with grime, and all alike. It had a number of detached three-storey houses possessed of basements and a patch of garden enclosed by laurel hedges; some respectable pubs; and it had the Royal Berkshire Hospital, which looked much more like a university than that establishment itself. Nearby, a narrow wooden porch abutted on to the road, and if you turned into this, you found yourself in a lobby with notice-boards and an office or two, much less imposing than the booking hall of any small country station. Beyond this lay the university: a red brick library with an ugly clock tower, a sort of outsize garden shed where examinations, dances and assemblies were held; and a straggle of low buildings, all of a temporary looking nature, which embraced lecture rooms and laboratories, linked by what were known as cloisters but were merely brick-floored pathways roofed by corrugated iron. The whole place had a newly spawned and makeshift appearance and lacked dignity, coherence or style.

Most of the students lived in halls of residence, and I had dreaded going to live in one with its inevitable rules and regulations and herding together. I was lucky; Reading had only two halls for women, and I had applied too late to get a place, so I was allocated to a hostel, or "approved lodging". This implied some rules and some herding, but much less; there were fewer than a score of us with a landlady, not a warden, in charge. The difference was subtle but profound; we were lodgers who provided her with a living rather than students to be kept in order. We occupied a tall, narrow, early Victorian house standing in a crescent just off the road, with a garden at the back containing a greenhouse, a pear tree, and a patch of lawn large enough for the cat to use without offence as a lavatory. There was a bowl of goldfish in the parlour, bamboo tables, lace curtains, prints of downcast lovers being rejected by drooping ladies apparently in nightgowns, and of cavalry charges in the Orient; anti-macassars, doilies, knicknacks and gas fires.

Each student had her own bed-sit; we shared a small sitting-room that had a balcony, an upright piano, a threadbare carpet and a grate that smoked, and ate together in a narrow room that always smelt of boiled cabbage. Most of us lived on scholar-ships considered lavish if they amounted to £100 a year. Even in those days of penny postage, threepenny loaves and nothing costing over sixpence in Woolworth's, this would not cover board, tuition fees and all the extras for a year, and everyone was permanently broke. Most of us bought our clothes second-hand and kept them, repeatedly mended, until they wore out; we darned our cotton stockings, had our shoes re-soled by cobblers in back streets, made one coat last for years and seldom smoked unless offered a cigarette by someone richer than our-selves. The men were poor too, but not quite so poor because their scholarships were larger and their families rightly regarded them as much better investments; for male graduates jobs were much easier to get, and the pay invariably higher.

Girls were in the fortunate position of being heavily out-numbered by men; invitations to Students' Union dances were therefore probable, though not inevitable, since a great many of the men did not go to dances because they had no dinner jackets and could not afford to hire them. Scruffy as we all were, dinner jackets at S.U. dances were essential, as were evening dresses, generally home-made, for the girls. In agriculture, which was my school, the sex ratio was even wider; there was only one other female freshman in my year, and about thirty men.

I soon discovered that, as in all walks of English life, this unpretentious university of some eight hundred lower middle class students was honeycombed with subtle snobberies. There was a pecking order among studies as well as among people; agriculture ranked high, not because farming was regarded as a snob pursuit—very few of the "agri" students were likely to plough a furrow or hoe a field of roots, and we had no sons of landowners—but because most of the graduates would join the staff of some local authority or government department, the latter often in the Empire as it then was. They would go forth to romantic sounding places like Nigeria and the Gold Coast, Barbados and Fiji, Tanganyika and the Solomons, where they would enjoy a most enviable status with bungalows, servants and sundowners, and become bronzed and manly in topees and shorts. While an agricultural officer ranked lower in the colonial hierarchy than a District Commissioner, he came well above the Public Works Department man; he could look for reasonable pay, excellent leave and a nice pension after twenty-five years' service, when he would be not much above forty-five.

So to be an "agri" was all right, and so was a "horti"; pure scientists, historians and classicists occupied a middle range, and at the bottom, I regret to say, came the future teachers, who read for a two-years' diploma instead of for a three or four-years' degree. Why future teachers should have been so poorly thought of, I do not know—I suppose because they were so poorly paid. "Edu's" tended to cluster together looking earnest, pallid (probably from malnutrition) and even more drearily dressed than the rest of us; to dodge coffees in the Buttery because twopence was beyond their means; and, if girls, to live at a remote hall called St. George's that no one else ever visited. The smart hall was St. Andrew's, just among the men it was Wantage, with St. Patrick's in second place. Occupants of "approved lodgings", such as myself, were loosely banded together, mainly for purposes of sport, in a non-existent hall called St. David's, whose only physical presence was a room in a dark and rather smelly house off the London Road which had a metered gas fire and a ping-pong table and where, on certain

4

evenings of the week, between five and ten, we were entitled to foregather. Very few of us did.

Whatever I had expected of a university—and my notions were exceedingly vague—I was disappointed. Wisdom, learning, scholarship—shades of Socrates and Erasmus, even of Jowett and Jeans—seemed even more remote than they had been in Africa; nor did any of my fellow students appear to be selflessly dedicated to the pursuit of knowledge. Most of the men were more interested in the pursuit of balls; the manly ones smoked pipes, wore plus-fours and ties with stripes denoting various clubs (not schools, we had virtually no public school-boys) and clustered together in the Buttery over coffee, tilting back their chairs at dangerous angles and now and then emitting guffaws suggestive of dirty stories, though probably arising from some exchange of personal remarks. In the Buttery, segregation of the sexes was pretty well complete, certainly among freshmen; now and again a third-year couple might be seen together, but this was considered if not exactly brazen, well on the flaunting side. People of opposite sexes who knew each other quite well would barely exchange nods in the Buttery, at least in the mornings; a cup of tea together in the afternoon after dissecting a frog or analysing soil samples was more permissible.

Any young woman of passable looks and a supply of what was then known as "it" was sure of a substantial following. In my digs, for example, there was a sought-after student named Snugg. She had a neatly shaped head which she kept tidily shingled, and an enviable amount of self-assurance. Snugg—we called each other by our surnames, like the men, a custom we shared, I think, only with convicts—Snugg was in her third year and often seen in the company of the captain of rugger. Turner was not only lord of the Fifteen but he was reading agriculture, had a job lined up in the colonies, held office in the Students' Union, and was said to drink a lot of beer; so he was one of the social princes. We envied Snugg her conquest, and admired the brushed good looks of Turner, whose dark hair grew to a point above his forehead, whose skin was clear and healthy and who had wide shoulders and narrow hips—an athlete's figure. The envious held that he was thrown away on

Snugg, who gave herself airs, and was apt to introduce into the conversation topics like hunt balls, point-to-points, first nights, presentations at court and cousins in the Foreign Office. She came from Birmingham, and undoubtedly drew her knowledge of these matters from the pages of the glossy magazines; so we were unimpressed, and found such conversations boring.

The first Students' Union dance took place soon after the start of the academic year. Tickets, so far as I remember, were three-and-six, including supper in the Buttery. The dances themselves were held in the outsize garden shed. The deal floor, rough and splintered and marked with ink stains from the pens of agonized examinees, was sprinkled for the occasion with french chalk which formed treacherous patches on which you were liable to slip and twist an ankle. Hard, straight-backed examination chairs were ranged along the walls in stiff military rows. From the iron girders of the roof dangled fly-spotted lightbulbs swathed in coloured crinkled paper. The hired band gave of its best, and a Master of Ceremonies, wearing a carnation, at intervals announced a Paul Jones. Between dances, you walked about in cloisters swept by gusts of icy wind that wrecked your hair-do and chilled your bones. If you wanted to sit out, you had to grope your way into a dark, bare lecture-room smelling of dust and chalk and possibly woodworm, or into a lab smelling of gas from leaking bunsen burners and formalin from jars of specimens such as stomach-worms of sheep and rabbit embryos.

Supper in the Buttery consisted of a small portion of tinned salmon with a very limp salad, vanilla ice cream and a pale, watery, lukewarm cup of coffee. Nothing alcoholic was provided, understandably considering the three-and-six, but there was no rule against bringing your own, and a few of the richer students put a half bottle of sweet sauterne on to the table; but as a rule the men moved off in batches to the nearest pub—there was one just across the way—while you awaited your partner's return on one of the hard exam chairs, unless someone else came up and asked you for the pleasure.

The pleasure! And yet, we did enjoy those dances. Years afterwards I saw a French film, *Carnet du Bal*, in which a dance in a small provincial town was seen first through the eyes of a sixteen-year-old girl, then of the mature woman that girl be-

came, returning for the début of her own daughter. In the first
scene the white-clad girls were graceful, fairylike and joyous,
the young men handsome, debonair and gay; the music en-
chanted, the scene sparkled, there was magic in the air. In
maturity, the re-visitor saw nothing but a bare assembly room,
gallumphing small-town maidens in cheap home-made frocks
matched by heavy-breathing, damp-palmed, spotty youths,
all rotating to excruciating music in their provincial stuffiness
and gaucherie. I thought immediately of our dances at Reading.
At eighteen, they had magic. God knows what one would
think of them now. But, of course, they have changed—even
more than we have, possibly.

As a rule, a fellow student was your partner, but you could, if
you wished, invite an outside guest. One Sunday, much to my
surprise, Jumbo Matheson turned up in a battered, wheezy old
two-seater, and took me for a drive. We did not find much to
say to each other, but little conversation was feasible anyway
in a windswept open coupé which rattled like an old tin can.
When we stopped for tea at an inn by the river, an effort had to
be made, and in a rather desperate moment I mentioned the
dance, thinking that it would be too far for him to come from
Portsmouth; to my consternation, he accepted. So there I was,
landed with Jumbo, quite nice but dull, and likely to be as much
a fish out of water at Reading, in a different way, as we had both
been at Montleven.

The evening came and with it Jumbo in his clanking car; he
looked spruce and quite presentable, despite a boil on his neck
that impeded his movements. Snugg had astonished me by inviting us to join her and Turner at supper. Why she should have
singled out a freshman of no account for such an honour I could
not fathom; possibly my partner's status as a Naval Officer
weighed with her, despite his attachment to a minesweeper
rather than to the Royal Yacht; perhaps, too, she was anxious
to avoid rivalry, and considered me a safe bet. She was very
possessive about Turner, and had to be constantly on guard
against predators—the penalty of having carried off such a prize.

In those days we did not dance the whole evening with one
partner, as became the custom later; we introduced our partners
to our friends, and everyone got busy with programme and

pencil as we stood about in the draughty cloisters. Jumbo, like me, found Snugg somewhat over-awing, although she tried to put him at his ease by introducing Cowes into the conversation. Unfortunately Jumbo had never witnessed the regatta, nor had he met an Admiral Pumphret whom Snugg claimed as a distant relative. He did his best, however, and was a good deal more forthcoming than he had been at Montleven, which had intimidated him as it had me; and although he was still apt sometimes to revert to Gertrude, I felt that he had more or less resigned himself to classing her as a hopeless passion to whom he would be faithful unto death in spirit, but not necessarily, at all times, in the flesh.

The other members of our supper party were Thomas and his partner, a student of dairying called Dando. Turner went about with three companions: Thomas, Corbett and Viney. They formed a little knot which they had named the Philosophers' Club; they sat together in the Buttery, drank together in the pub, in summer shared a boat on the river, in winter jaunts to London to see a show. Their lives were strenuous and distinguished; Corbett was the cricket captain, Thomas an athlete and a hockey star, Viney the captain of the O.T.C. and a member of the university eight. Viney was a stalwart, silent pipe-smoker, said to be shy and known as a woman-hater, or at any rate woman shunner, and did not attend the dance.

Dando was large, square, amiable and played lacrosse, and I could see that Jumbo found her rather heavy going; but eventually they found a common theme in dogs. Jumbo had a cocker spaniel to whom he was devoted, and Dando's parents bred bloodhounds in Somerset. That bloodhounds were in the least savage, she asserted with something approaching passion, was a wicked slander; they were gentle, kind, obedient and affectionate creatures, and, as mothers, the bitches were unsurpassed. "Expensive to keep, though," Jumbo suggested. "We get bullocks' heads cheap from the slaughter-house, and pigs' offal from the bacon factory."

Turner had no option but to inscribe his initials on my programme: two lots of two dances running, and a single towards the end, which took place at eleven sharp. I could not resist a tingle of excitement and an even more foolish feeling of triumph; everyone would envy me the partnership of Turner, and they might not all realize that he had had no choice in the matter. Turner looked inviting, to say the least; he was a graceful mover, brisk and self-assured, his black hair was sleeked with lotion and neatly cut and brushed. There was, in fact, something neat about him in all aspects, in his looks, his movements, even his clothes. This was his final year; soon he would be on his way to Trinidad, where all candidates for the colonial service spent another year studying tropical agriculture, before proceeding to some fortunate colony in Africa or the Pacific, where he would apply his skill to improving the lot of the natives, and in due course himself mount the ladder of success to a directorship of Agriculture in some colony such as Sierra Leone, Nyasaland or the New Hebrides.

Turner was a smooth dancer with a good, firm clasp between the shoulder-blades, straight-forward in his steps but light and nimble. Fortunately he did not want to talk while dancing, apart from the usual exchanges about floor and band; but during the interval, after he had fetched two very yellow lemonades, the need to converse had to be faced. Not for nothing were opening gambits generally described as breaking the ice.

"Was it you I saw out with the beagles on Thursday, round Corner's Brook?"

"I'm afraid I haven't beagled. I don't think I could run fast enough. Are you fond of it?"

"Well, it's good exercise."

"People seem to take a lot of exercise here."

This did not seem to be getting us anywhere. We walked along the cloisters, heads into the wind; here and there a Japanese lantern hitched on to a rafter lent a note of genteel gaiety. Above the clock-tower, which stuck up like a factory chimney, a half moon now and then appeared through clouds that were plodding rather than scudding across the sky.

"I hear you've made friends with Maisie."

"Maisie?"

"Snugg."

"I had no idea her name was Maisie."

"It isn't really, but it suits her. Do you like mine?"

"I don't know what it is."

"What would you like it to be?"

I had no idea whether I should say something plain like George, or try to be facetious with Marmaduke or Ferdinand. Turner had tucked his arm into mine, which was nice and warming, despite the wind which was niggling down my spine and chilling my knees. Had I seen his initials anywhere? A, B, C, D . . .

"Douglas," I suggested.

"Douglas it shall be. One should be named by one's friends, not one's parents; how can they tell with nothing but a mewling infant to go on? I like Douglas though it's Scotch and I'm anti sporrans and haggises and things. Tell me why Douglas."

"I don't know . . . Black. Black Douglas. I mean your eyebrows."

Turner gave a loud chortle, and my spirits soared. At least I had made him laugh. He had entrancing eyebrows and could raise each one separately, turning it into a V which created a quizzical expression. He put his arm round my shoulders and gave them a squeeze: comradely rather than amorous, but still a start, and we were approaching a darker stretch of cloister devoid of Japanese lanterns. But then, in the distance, we heard the music start.

"Once more unto the breach," said Turner, swinging me round; hopefully, I thought he spoke with a tinge of regret.

Our partners were standing by the door, Jumbo meekly, Snugg with a fixed smile suggesting the reverse of amusement. Turner whisked her off before she could speak.

"I like your friend," Jumbo said, "but she seems a bit edgy."

"I don't suppose she's keen on dogs."

"Well, we can't all be. Even Gertrude seems to get a bit impatient with them sometimes. Have you heard from her lately?"

"Oh, do let's leave Gert out of it for once."

Jumbo looked contrite. "I'm afraid I'm an awful bore. When are you coming to see *Periwinkle*?"

"I didn't know I'd been asked."

"Of course you've been asked. Now I've got the jalopy I could come and fetch you. We could make up a party, there's room for two in the dickie. I can bring oilskins if it's wet."

"Who do you want? Turner and Snugg?"

"Anyone you like. That bloodhound girl's not a bad sort. She says a daily dose of garlic after worming keeps them clear for months. Oh, sorry!"

We had bumped into a couple and nearly knocked them over; the girl lost her shoe and Jumbo retrieved it from among the feet of dancers much as if he had been his own spaniel after a winged partridge. She turned out to be a student of Fine Arts from my lodgings called Swift: a plumpish, rather blowsy looking extrovert with untidy hair, a loose-muscled face, slouching shoulders and floppy breasts. But she had fine eyes, the colour of a cornflower, an amiable smile, and an open-minded attitude towards her fellow-men; in fact her present partner was a swarthy, sleek-haired Oriental of some kind, possibly Egyptian or Levantine. She accepted Jumbo's apologies breezily.

"Rammed me amidships, what? Better than holing my bottom."

They pranced off, and Jumbo looked shocked. "Not quite the way to talk in front of a native," he said.

I had two more dances to look forward to with Turner, but when the first came round it was a tango. I had never learnt to tango, and it was not a dance you could pick up as you went along. I confessed my ignorance shamefacedly, but Turner did not tango either, it appeared. "We'll sit it out," he said.

This seemed too good to be true; and it was. Dando and Thomas were retreating for the same reason, while the band thumped away in what it intended to be a throbbing Latin rhythm with a hint of black shawls and castanets, and so we drifted together into the bursar's office, which had been equipped with extra chairs. By now the wind had freshened to gale force and was driving icy rain through the cloisters, and we were all thankful when the South American interlude ended and we were back on familiar ground with a polka to warm us up, and nice jiggly music. Jumbo would have a wet drive back to Portsmouth in his open coupé.

"Hasn't it got a hood?"

"I only gave ten pounds for her. But I like plenty of fresh air."

He saw me home through the downpour, which discouraged

lingering farewells, and said that he would run over one Sunday
to take me to his vessel, of which he seemed almost as fond as of
his spaniel; or, if I preferred it, we might run up to town and
go to a *thé dansant*. I was not quite sure what a *thé dansant* was,
but it sounded gay.

Chapter Five

O N the Sunday following a dance it was customary to walk with your partner along the tow-path by the river bank to the village of Sonning, about three miles up-stream, and have tea at the White Hart or the French Horn. For sheer ugliness it would be impossible to beat that stretch of country now, overspread by unplanned factories, bungalows, blocks of flats, transformers, filling stations—a sort of industrial vomit; even then, in winter, the walk was less romantic than bracing, with a wet gale blustering from the direction of East Anglia and the North Sea, and Siberia beyond. Nevertheless it had this sentimental implication, that an invitation to Sunday tea at Sonning amounted to a declaration of interest, if no more, on the part of a young man.

In those days it was a pleasant tow-path, with many noble trees, and the river, shining like quicksilver, bending the reeds, eddying round knotted tree-roots and sometimes dividing to embrace a small, low island, and carrying along branches that bobbed and jinked as if they had a life of their own. Dabchicks ducked and dived beneath the banks, sometimes a water-vole rippled the surface and often there were swans, majestically heraldic and, escorted by their grey shadows, looking bad-tempered with a dark band across the base of their bills. One could imagine the strong, hairy-legged horses plodding along with barges in tow, but they were gone; vessels propelled by chugging engines fussed by, drawing barges loaded with coal or timber and spreading behind them a fan of ripples that died quietly in the muddy banks, and rocked the reeds and driftwood with a gentle motion.

Whether it was the icy winds that had assailed the cloisters, or something wrong with the tinned salmon, or for some other reason, Snugg woke up on Sunday morning with a temperature, a sore throat and collywobbles. For her, no walk to Sonning; it was raining anyway. It seemed to rain a great deal in Reading. One of the minor mysteries of English life, to me, was how the

English skies could weep all day and shed so little actual water
—less than an African sky would toss off in a couple of minutes.
Climate and people in the British Isles never did anything by
halves, but by very small fractions, as if looking the other way
and half ashamed of doing them.

"Turner gave me this for you," Swift said at lunch—Sunday
dinner, rather, with a leg of mutton, pallid cabbage, underdone
roast potatoes, lumpy gravy and a choice of stewed prunes and
blancmange. "This" was a note folded into a triangle, on ruled
paper, in a small, sloping hand, inviting me to have a spot of
tea at the White Hart, and signed Douglas. Can hearts really
leap? That is what they sometimes feel like, just as on other
occasions they really do seem to sink. I tried to look aloof and
unconcerned, but Swift grinned and gave a wink.

What to wear? A mac and thick shoes were obvious, and, one
must suppose, a tweed skirt; but this was dreadfully dull. There
was my check two-piece, but this came out almost every day. I
had extended my wardrobe by one or two visits to helpful
places called Guinea Shops, where it was comforting to know
that nothing *could* cost more than this sum, and astonishing
what you could get for it. My latest purchase had been a dress
entirely made of brown lace, but this seemed a little flimsy—
more suited to a *thé dansant*, should Jumbo pursue his sugges-
tion, than to a tramp along the tow-path. I had a red velvet,
but that did not seem right either. In the end I fell back on the
check. During the walk, it mattered little what you had on
underneath mac and muffler and, of course, a cloche hat. You
never went far without a cloche hat.

A malignant wind raced along the tow-path, tearing at mac
and cloche and unprotected legs, and at the reeds and wires and
bits of crumpled paper, convulsing the naked trees and lashing
at the surface of the muddy water. Turner strode along with the
ends of his black and purple muffler flying, wisely clad in plus-
fours but bare-headed, clenching a pipe. Light conversation
stood little chance.

At the White Hart they served you hot toasted tea-cakes,
scones, cress sandwiches and plain bread-and-butter, followed
by a wide choice of cakes, in a dark, oak-panelled lounge; in
summer, you had tea on a lawn sloping down to the river.

Luckily this was not summer. In summer it rained just as much, but you had to pretend it was not raining—the downpour was called a shower, to distinguish it from rain, although you got just as wet.

Your main occupation, once seated at your table, was to see if anyone you knew was there and, if so, with whom. The only acquaintance I could see was Swift, accompanied by her Oriental partner of the night before.

"That chap's an Arab," Turner said.

"Oh. What's he doing here?"

"At the moment, burning his fingers I should say."

"Burning his fingers?"

I made a mental note to try not to repeat a companion's last remark, when I did not immediately grasp its meaning; whenever other people did this, I was irritated.

"Hot stuff," Turner said, glancing at Swift and raising one of his eyebrows.

The Arab was a disappointment: small and fat, with a pudgy nose and a complexion like an over-boiled suet pudding. You could not imagine him saying farewell to his steed with any emotion, except insofar as its price was concerned. "Far are the shades of Arabia, where the princes ride at noon." On Sunday afternoon at the White Hart they were farther than ever.

"I wonder what he's reading."

"Commerce."

There was a diploma in commerce, obviously not a subject to be studied at Oxford. We took it for granted, without any hard feelings, that no one would be at Reading if he could possibly have got a place at Oxford; this, I suppose, was the main reason why things like dairying and horticulture, of whose very existence the older university was no doubt unaware, had a high snob rating with us; at least the horticulturalists and dairyists had not tried elsewhere and failed. Evidently commerce was in the same category; you could not imagine it as a field of study at Balliol, Magdalen or Christ Church.

"I wonder what Swift sees in him."

"Dough," replied Turner. "Rolling in it, they say. Probably got a harem tucked away in Constantinople or Samarkand or somewhere."

"They sound exciting, those places, but I don't suppose they really are."

"I daresay Reading sounds exciting if you live in Constantinople."

"It hasn't got the Orient Express."

"Well, there's the Thames."

For one of the world's major rivers, with all that history, the Thames had been a disappointment too. It was small, and lacked grandeur—no falls, cataracts or rapids, no mighty gorges, no forest-covered banks, and very dull shipping, just those flat, dirty barges, a few scullers and punts, a motor-launch or two; no paddle steamers, junks, sampans or war canoes.

"The eight was out yesterday," Turner said. "Shaping well so far, Viney reports. Might have a chance in the Ladies Plate this year."

So far as I could remember, Turner took no part in rowing, but it was hard to recall who did what, in the field of sport, among the four Philosophers. I longed to know more about Turner, personal things, but had no idea how to find out except by asking questions, which sounded like a cross-examination.

"I suppose you live in England?"

Turner raised his one v-shaped eyebrow; it made him look faintly diabolic, although his countenance was too guileless to reflect true satanic qualities. His clear skin reminded me, for some obscure reason, of a grain of ripe wheat.

"Where else? Sceptred isle, teeming womb, nation of shopkeepers, birthplace of the Durham Ox. As a matter of fact I come from Dover."

Dover. At least I had heard of it. Soles, cliffs, Cinque Ports . . . "I suppose you've been to France?"

"Never. The food's too rich and I hate being seasick. Stick to dry land and roast beef."

I felt that I had said something unpatriotic. "Do the French play rugger?"

"Not so as you'd notice. A little soccer I believe. I think their main thing is bicycling."

"Have you always lived in Dover?"

"More or less. On and off. Had a spell once in Cardiff."

Even when it came to where they lived, a simple matter you

would think, the natives of England seemed unwilling to commit themselves. I thought that if he had been an African, by now I
should know not only where he lived and the circumstances of
his family but all about his uncles, crops and goats and what
he was paying for a wife.

"Your father," I began, and thought better of it. "More tea?"

"It's cold by now I expect. We could get some hot water."
I had been neglecting my feminine duties. When Turner
beckoned to the waitress, she came, if not with a smile at least
without a scowl. He was like that. Swift had been trying for
some time, without success, to attract her attention. Presently
Swift came over to our table with her Arab in tow.

"This is Abdul." He insisted on shaking hands. His hand
was moist and pudgy and his black, sleeked-back hair smelt
spicy. Swift looked at me and added: "He comes from Alexandria. You've been in those parts, haven't you?"

"Not in Egypt, I'm afraid."

"Alexandria is a fine city," Abdul pronounced. "Very big,
very growing, very good trade."

"Yes."

"The English sailors like it when they come in their warships."

"Abdul's thinking of buying a car," Swift observed. Turner,
removing his pipe, for the first time looked interested.

"What make?"

"Oh, I suppose a baby Austin or something like that."

"Why not an M.G. or a Riley?"

They entered into a discussion about Abdul's future car in
which Abdul took no part; instead, he gazed at Swift with his
soft lips slightly apart, his eyes round and black and, I thought,
sad as a monkey's. His skin was thick-pored and slightly pitted.
Abdul was no beauty and had, as we put the matter, got it
badly, or so I judged from the intensity of his gaze at Swift, as
if he wanted to gobble her up. He wore a cornelian ring on one
of his fat toffee-coloured fingers, and a pin mounted with a
clear brown gem-stone in his striped tie.

Abdul was not in the least like any of the Arabs I had hitherto
encountered, who had been dressed in long white robes and
loosely wound turbans, and had wives swaddled in yards of
black material in which narrow slits had been cut for kohl-

rimmed eyes. If he was a Muslim, he could have four wives. I wondered whether he had any already, and planned to add Swift to their number. She would be a disturbing influence in a harem. It was a pity one could broach none of the interesting topics.

"Do you like Reading?"

Abdul withdrew his gaze from Swift with an obvious effort. "Yes, thank you, very nice."

"I expect you find it cold after Egypt."

He gave a deep sniff, like someone taking snuff, and spread his hands. "Yes, but I expected. I do not yet see any snow."

"Nor have I seen any as a matter of fact. They say it doesn't snow much in the Thames valley."

"This is the Thames valley?"

"I believe so."

"I have seen it on the buses. They are good buses. Why are they all red?"

"I don't know."

By now Swift and Turner had decided on an Oldsmobile. "You want something with a bit of build and guts to it," Turner said. "Then you could take it home when you go."

"Oh, yes. Home . . ."

Did he look wistful, resentful or indifferent? Impossible to tell. His sad eyes turned back to Swift.

"Abdul's home sounds very crowded," she said. "How many sisters have you got, Abdul?"

He shrugged his shoulders. "Seven, perhaps."

"What do you mean by perhaps?"

"My mother does not write very often."

"And of course brothers, step-brothers, half-sisters, uncles, aunts, brothers-in-law, nieces and nephews," Swift added.

"He needs a bus, really, to take back."

"We'd better be getting back ourselves," Turner said, stretching his arms and shoulders to an extent that endangered the ladder-back of the White Hart's olde-world chair. "Mustn't be late for opening time."

The waitress brought two bills and Abdul tried to pay both— a *gaffe* which irritated Turner. "These blokes always try to throw their weight about," he remarked as we tacked into the gale on our homeward tramp. The gale had become even more ferocious, blustering at our knees and macs and hair, and at Turner's scarf, with a vindictiveness that seemed personal, somehow—it was after me, and him perhaps, and no one else. You wanted to answer back but there was no way. The leaden sky was darkening, the boughs creaking and threshing, everything was sodden; even the lethargic waters of the river gave a gurgle now and then. I thought longingly of the red buses which no doubt sometimes plied, even on Sundays, in the direction of Reading; but this tow-path tramp was part of the ritual. Poor Abdul: it must seem a long way from his seven sisters, perhaps eight by now, the spicy curries, the sweet thick coffee and the sunlit Nile.

"I suppose you'll go somewhere hot when you go down," I remarked.

"Eventually, no doubt. But not at once I hope."

"I meant the colonies."

"Oh, I daresay. Teach the blacks to grow sorghum and mangosteens. Nothing I don't know about mangosteens."

I suppose it is the motor car that has liberalized the morals of students; and the fact that students have become rich enough to own cars, or at least to know someone who does. As soon as you are in a motor car, where you can sit down and keep warm, you can carry your canoodling to any lengths you like, according to your taste, spirit of enterprise and degree of caution. People talk a lot about the decline of morals, collapse of religion and so on among the young. It was not religion or morality that kept most of us relatively chaste, but lack of facilities. What could we do on a muddy tow-path in a wet gale on a Sunday evening swathed in macs and blue with cold, even when strengthened by iced cakes? Or when we bade our escort goodnight in the hostel's dingy hall, under a dangling light-bulb beside the gong, bamboo table and cuckoo clock, amid a smell of cabbages? A motor car would have been like some heavenly chariot to us all; caution and morality would have melted like rime before the sun—even caution, then a much stronger deterrent to amorous experiment than it later became, contraceptives being more crude and less widely retailed.

We were all nervous about starting babies and, if things got as far as that, more inhibited than girls later became about checking up before-hand that our partner had a french letter. Even if he had, there was the risk of its splitting. So altogether it was not surprising that most of us, I believe, remained virgins during our students days or, if we did not, changed our status in the vacs rather than in term-time. People were far more reticent than a later generation was to become. There were exceptions; Swift, for instance, was said, I do not know by whom—herself perhaps?—to have "gone the whole hog", a reputation which gave her a certain *réclame* in our eyes. I have no doubt there was a religious side to life at Reading but recall no evidence of it, and never entered a church when I was there. So it was not that which kept us on the rails, insofar as we stuck to them: rails most of us were only too anxious to leave. What was the point of being young if you did not find out all you could about living? To do so was our duty, we believed.

The tow-path offered little opportunity, however. It traversed a small wood, or remnants of a wood, not far from where the houses began, and there Turner stopped to put his pipe away, took my arm and pulled me close to him. Out of loyalty to Snugg, I felt, I should have at this point drawn back demurely but did not. His cheek felt as cold and wet as mine but at least his lips were warm and his embrace consoling. But both of us were too well insulated by macs, sweaters, mufflers and wet woollen gloves to make much progress down the primrose path. We said goodnight sedately by the front door and I went in with a song in my heart, as the song said. I knew it would be a come-down to retreat to my barely furnished room inadequately heated by a metered gas fire, and to our cold Sunday tinned salmon and stewed prunes; and it was.

"How's Snugg?"

"Better. Her temperature's down."

So my brief hour was over, like the butterfly's. Turner had said I was to call him Douglas, but that was not his name. Snugg called him Joe.

5

Chapter Six

ON balance, I did not welcome the vacations. Nathan's Orchard was even colder and damper than Reading, it was certainly gloomier and there was less to do. No cosy sessions in the Buttery between lectures, no gossip that, trivial as it was, drew you into a world in which you had a place, however lowly; no satisfying sessions in the library dipping into subjects ranging from psychoanalysis to Egyptology, Chinese poetry to astronomy, Plato's *Republic* to Scandinavian mythology, having in common nothing but their total irrelevance to my own course of studies; no visits to the cinema where seats cost ninepence, unless a friend in funds took you to the one-and-fours; no Philosophers' Club and above all no Turner.

Snugg had resumed her rights, so I had not enjoyed another walk to Sonning; nevertheless I had exchanged a word or two with him in the cloisters, and spent several afternoons, wrapped from head to foot in woollies, coats and mufflers, watching rugger. After the first few minutes it became impossible to distinguish one player from another, since everyone was coated with mud; the wind chapped my skin, my nose was running and my feet like blocks of ice; but there I stood, amid a thin fringe of spectators, eyes fixed upon anonymous brown creatures clinging together like clusters of enormous bees, until suddenly the swarm broke up and there was an agitated scurrying to and fro ended by a whistle and a re-clustering of the enormous brown bees. At intervals we shouted phrases of encouragement, advice or disgust, inaudible to the bees, that sounded more like the protests of an animal in pain than any rational and human noise.

Somewhere in amongst them all was Turner, shoving and leaping and flinging himself face-downwards into the mud, but it was quite impossible to see which he was, and there was no chance that he would recognize me; so why I trudged up Redlands Road on those bleak afternoons I do not know, unless it was in the hope that I might, on one of our cloister encounters, be able to say: "I saw you score that marvellous try against

Bradfield on Thursday." Such an opportunity had not arisen yet, but you never knew.

At Nathan's Orchard I was glad to see Kate again. She, too, had returned for the holidays with considerable reluctance; only a total lack of cash, and an inability to borrow any more than she had borrowed already, had restored her to her family. The art school, I gathered, was a success, although Kate was reticent about it; she always was a dark horse. "It's nothing like the Slade, of course," she said, leaving me little the wiser, since I did not know what the Slade was like either. Kate's school was a small affair, run by a Miss Eileen Hapgold, A.R.A., a lady in her seventies who said in the prospectus that she had studied under Alma-Tadema and Renoir. It seemed an odd combination. "Of course she was a model really," Kate said.

Uncle Jack had agreed with great reluctance to let Kate "try it out" because an aunt of his had once met Alma-Tadema and said that he was "quite the gentleman," and because Miss Hapgold had, on demand, sent references, one from a clergyman and one from the manager of a bank. Or so they had described themselves on the letters; there was nothing to prove it, and Kate had remarked: "I expect Aggie wrote them." Aggie was Miss Hapgold's companion. Many, many years ago, she had been on the stage. Another point in Miss Hapgold's favour was that her school was not in London but outside it, and not quite in Middlesex but in Bucks. "There was a branch of the Gaskoyne-Maynells in Buckinghamshire," Uncle Jack had said. "Quite decent folk, they were." When Kate returned, with her few possessions in a brown paper parcel, a folder of sketches under her arm and in a very short kind of smock, her father's first words were: "Did you run across the Gaskoyne-Maynells in Buckinghamshire? They used to hunt with the Grafton." Kate, whose academy was not far from Bushey Park, replied that she had not. "Pity."

Because of Uncle Jack's hostility, Aunt Madge became a strong supporter of Miss Hapgold. "Our family has always had an artistic streak," she said. Uncle Jack shot back his wrinkled brow. "May I ask whom you have in mind?" "Great-grandmother Helen was painted by Lely. And Aunt Octavia had one of the finest collections of Ming in England." "It was her

father-in-law's," Uncle Jack said coldly. "She only inherited it."
"You'll eat your words," Aunt Madge prophesied, "when Kate
is hung in the Academy." "I shall be thankful if it's only in the
Academy," Uncle Jack replied.

"What does this Aggie do?" Aunt Madge inquired of Kate.
"Does she paint too?" "She exercises the pug." "There, what
did I tell you?" my aunt said triumphantly. "Pugs are all right.
Mama had a pug. Of course Miss Hapgold's all right."

The little I could glean from Kate's random remarks suggested that she herself was not often at Miss Hapgold's establishment. Rules seemed to be lax, if indeed there were any, and
trains ran frequently from Bushey Park to Piccadilly Circus and
Leicester Square. Names that I had seen on gramophone
records, or read in newspapers, cropped up now and again, like
Hutch and Nancy Cunard, Noël Coward and Duke Ellington,
Elsa Maxwell and Augustus John and Mrs. Merrick, Brenda
Dean Paul and others I have forgotten, for their fame was short-
lived, but at the time stood high in the world of night-clubs,
jazz joints and dives of the Soho—Wardour Street—Shaftesbury
Avenue—Rupert Street area, even as far afield as the Totten-
ham Court Road. Here, indeed, was Life, and Kate seemed to
have made contact with it; but then you never could be sure;
her imagination, fertilized by all these new experiences, had
put out fresh shoots, and, as in the case of Miss Hapgold's
references, there was no way of checking. She was only just
seventeen.

By comparison, my life at Reading seemed very drab. "I hope
you have not become a bluestocking," Uncle Jack remarked.
This did not seem to me to be one of the serious hazards at
Reading, at any rate in the faculty of agriculture. "What's it all
got to do with farming, I should like to know?" Aunt Madge
demanded. "None of those long-haired professors know a swede
from a sheep. All they do is torture frogs." "Torture frogs?"
"I've read about it. It's disgusting. I'd like to see one of those
professors ploughing Lower Cornground in a wet autumn and
an east wind with Bollocks and Emma, when Emma's in one
of her moods." Emma was one of the heavy shire horses the
farm depended on, famous for her awkward moods.

"Professor Pennington——" I began, but Aunt Madge cut

me short. "Professor this professor that, it was a great mistake doing away with the penal settlements in Australia, that's where they all ought to be." I had been going to say that Sidney Pennington, although a professor, was a most practical man, and probably could have made a good job of Lower Cornground with Bollocks and Emma; large, loosely built, white-haired and healthy-looking, with a north country accent—I think he came from Cumberland—his lectures were full of instructions about how to rot farmyard manure, estimate the needed quantities of basic slag, improve a pasture, follow the Norfolk Four-Course Rotation and, when it came to breeding livestock, the great merits of the Durham Ox, which had toured the country in a specially constructed coach in the early 1800s to demonstrate the new look in beef cattle achieved by breeders who made incest (among their livestock) obligatory. Also, the professor was accompanied everywhere by a small and shaggy white terrier. If I had only been able to get around to the terrier I might have changed my aunt's opinion of all professors, but I never could.

Gertrude, Kate and I were invited to Boscombe for Christmas, to stay with Uncle Rufus and Aunt Lilli; Joanna had to stay at home with suspected German measles. Uncle Rufus was the eldest brother of my mother and of Aunt Madge, and had inherited Boscombe, which was about five miles away. To us he resembled some large, grumpy and morose bear. He was not red-headed, as he should have been from his name, but bald, and had a queer, bony face with flared nostrils like a monkey's; he spoke little, and when he did, spoke very slowly, as if it hurt him to do so, ending his remarks with a sort of upward grunt. I know now he was a patient man, and paralysed by shyness; but of that we had no inkling. He was a brilliant horseman, and passionately devoted to fox-hunting; everything took second place to the hounds, including his family. In fact the only time he took much notice of his family was when he had turned us into a pack of hounds and hunted us up and down the corridors and through the empty rooms of Boscombe in a game called "fox". When Ralph was at home, he was always the fox, because he knew the house so well. Ralph was Uncle Rufus's only son; his only child, in fact.

Boscombe was enormous, and the whole of the top floor had never been occupied because the house had never been finished. There was no furniture up there, no carpets, no electric light; just bare boards, empty echoing rooms, dark corners, unexpected stairways, mysteriously slamming doors, damp and dust, and long shadows thrown by a questing torch. It was ideal terrain for a pack of human hounds to hunt through stealthily in darkness, "drawing" room after room with a delicious tingling of the skin, alert for the least tell-tale creak of boards or distant footfall, while Uncle Rufus, hunting horn in hand, directed us with occasional phrases like "lew in there, Challenger," and "sick 'em out, Vengeance," delivered in a raucous whisper.

If the quarry was sighted—a quick glimpse of a shadow flickering away at the far end of the corridor—then pandemonium erupted; the horn's broken summons resounded through the house, my uncle delivered himself of a mighty roaring "tally-ho", wails of "gone awa-a-a-a-y" practically lifted the rafters and the whole pack pelted off after the retreating figure who generally eluded us, sometimes by a clever piece of doubling back among rooms opening out of each other, or by crouching in some cupboard while the human pack swept by.

When Ralph was fox we knew it would be an hour at least before we cornered him, if we ever did; sometimes the hunt was called off without a "kill" and Ralph would emerge, grinning, from a coal-bunker in the boiler-room perhaps, or a linen press on a landing, or once from right underneath a drawing-room sofa. On another occasion we ran him to earth, or rather to sky, up a rope ladder that dangled from the ceiling of a room in the basement used as a gymnasium; he pulled the rope up after him so that we could not get at him, but equally he could not get down without being caught. We stood below him baying ferociously until our throats were sore. After a game we all trooped off, panting and dishevelled, to the dining room to demolish an enormous tea. Sometimes we numbered fifteen or twenty of all ages from about eight or nine upwards, until Ralph left school and went to Oxford, and everyone suddenly became grown-up.

By the time I returned to Boscombe on vacations from Reading, such strenuous childhood games had been replaced by theatricals, organized by Aunt Lilli. Rufus had nothing to do with them, just as Lilli had had nothing to do with "fox". She used to put her small, brittle hands over her ears and shut her eyes and cry: "That dreadful horn, those awful noises like howling dervishes, if you knew how they torture my nerves!" Rufus paid no attention. Now, with the theatricals, she and her side of the family came into their own.

It was said that Rufus had announced his betrothal in a note to his parent which read: "Dear Father, I am engaged to a Miss Bauer who has £2,000 a year." Rufus was then in a cavalry regiment and it was understood that in due course he would leave, settle down at Boscombe to the life of a country squire with a reasonable rent-roll, a pack of hounds, some decent shooting and a home farm, and marry the healthy daughter of some neighbouring squire, a girl who rode well to hounds, understood the servants, had green fingers and knew a badger's sett from a fox's earth. This was no doubt his own intention, too. Rufus loved Boscombe, he knew every copse and covert on the place, the character of every field and hedge, the circumstances of every tenant and tenant's family, the state of every roof. The clay soils and tall oaks of Boscombe were the warp and woof of his being, and the path on which destiny had set his feet the only path he ever wanted to travel. He was no rebel. Unfortunately, at a dance in London, he met and fell in love with Lilli Bauer. If there was a single girl in England more unsuited to espouse the future squire of Boscombe, she would have been hard to discover. But he was twenty-two, his heart had surrendered and there was nothing to be done—except to marry Miss Bauer, which in due course, and despite his parent's sorrow, he did, to live more or less unhappily ever after.

Not that there was anything, in particular, against Lilli. She was, I think without exception, the loveliest woman I have ever seen. She was tiny, an animated doll, and beautifully made —like some little slender bird, one of those lily-trotters; like a freesia, like a feather. Everything about her was neat and delicate and fragile. She always smelt delicious. Her only large features were her eyes. These were china-blue, round, and innocent. Otherwise the scale was miniature; she took size three in shoes and cannot have weighed more than six stone. Rufus was a hulking sort of man—not especially tall, but with heavy bones. Lilli's were sparrow-like.

How did anyone whose name suggested an origin stolidly Germanic, or possibly Dutch, come to be so exotic, so *petite*? It was said that her mother had been Russian, or perhaps half Russian, and no one knew what dubious strains had gone into the making of this family of City merchants and bankers. No one knew anything about them at all, except that they belonged to the City, that jungle far more alien to any Devon squire than jungles of Bengal or the Amazon, where at least he would have had a gun in his hands and known what to expect of a tiger or a puma. You could not possibly know what to expect of people with names like Bauer, Kruttsschnitt or Goldsmitt, or Guggenheim and Kleinwort, Messel or Lazard, except that they were likely to be clever and rich.

There was nothing, of course, against being rich, in fact sons and heirs to country properties were always being told that they must marry money; but by money their fathers meant either a fat rent-roll, or safe investments in the Funds and possibly the Railways. Mysterious dealings in the City were another matter. So the banner which Rufus's little note to his father waved, as it were, over his intentions, that Lilli had £2,000 a year, failed to mollify his parent. His marriage was accepted, in advance, as an almost total disaster.

This was, of course, his family's view. What was the Bauers'? No one seemed to know or care. Lilli's mother, the Russian or half-Russian, had died giving birth to Lilli. There was one elder sister called Joy, married to a stockbroker named Mellanby, and a brother in America. Lilli's father had married again. I never saw him, and nor did Rufus, except presumably at his own wedding. Lilli used now and again to vanish to London—Rufus went there about once every three years, to fit a new pair of hunting boots—and commune with her relations, some of whom used to visit Boscombe. This was seldom a success.

Rufus disliked them all, especially Joy, who in the past had cheered for women's suffrage and in the present supported the demands of coal-miners, trade unions and even socialists; she had the temerity to argue with her brother-in-law, and to attack fox-hunting, and to be a pacifist. No wonder the atmosphere was strained and awkward when Joy was at Boscombe, and it was not much better when various nieces, nephews and cousins appeared. Rufus simply ignored them, and Boscombe was big enough for them to keep out of his way. This they were only too anxious to do, but Lilli played it all up. "Here comes nunc," she would warn them in conspiratorial tones. "Careful, children, melt into the landscape"; or, putting a finger to her lips: "Ssh-sh, everyone, the bear's in his lair, don't wake him." The nieces and nephews would giggle and walk on tiptoe, and of course Rufus saw and heard all this perfectly well; sometimes his rather mottled flesh would darken and his eyes grow hard. He never said anything, but grew more and more morose and alarming, like a thundercloud hanging over the house.

Now and then, Lilli would succumb to the temptation to torment him. "How many harmless little foxes have you *murdered* today?" she would demand when he came in, mud-bespattered and hungry, from a day in the squelching Devon mud; or, on his return from a session on the local Bench, she would exclaim: "I hope you've enjoyed flinging all those poor unemployed, half-starving men with hungry families into prison!" Lilli was a great one for underdogs and, like her sister, an ardent pacifist. Aunt Madge said that in the war she had filled Boscombe with refugees, and when Rufus had come home on leave from the trenches her first words of greeting had been: "How can you hold up your head for shame? You're nothing but a wicked *murderer!*" Rufus, Aunt Madge said, had stood and looked at Lilli as if he had been turned to stone and then, without a word, marched out of the door and down the steps and caught the first train to London, and spent his leave at his club.

Aunt Madge so disliked Lilli that she might have invented this story, or at the least exaggerated. Lilli, I think, was stupid rather than deliberately cruel. Once she collected up the various children who were in the house, led them stealthily to Rufus's bedroom and egged them on to make an apple-pie bed and devise various booby traps. Everyone thought it very funny but Kate and I did not join in, I suppose out of a vague sense of family loyalty. Not that we were fond of Rufus, but we mistrusted the Bauers, and thought it all rather childish. "After all, Boscombe is *his*," Kate said.

A portrait of our grandfather hung over the stairs and consisted mainly of a bushy black beard. The eyes that peered out of it, insofar as they could be seen, had a distinct twinkle. He had been a shy man, I believe, like his son Rufus, but not so morose, probably because he had a happier marriage; his wife was Irish, married at the age of thirty-seven, quickly had five children and then retired to a sofa in the drawing-room with a lot of shawls, novels, pugs and chocolates and, attended by ladies' maids and footmen, refused to stir again so long as the family remained at Boscombe. Why they left it was a sad and strange tale.

When my grandfather had, in his turn, inherited Boscombe, the residence had been a small, compact and, according to surviving sketches, altogether charming manor house, reconstructed about the time of Queen Anne. All through the eighteenth century, and until the last quarter of the nineteenth, this had been perfectly adequate for the squires of Boscombe, never an ambitious lot. In the latter part of the nineteenth century, an extraordinary fit of *folies de grandeur* overtook many country squires. Houses that had for centuries accommodated their ample families and equally ample retinues suddenly did not seem grand enough, and had to be pulled down and replaced by something much larger, more pretentious and infinitely uglier, all in red brick with balustrades and turrets. In part, this may have been because so many City gents who had made fortunes out of industry, trade and finance bought country properties and set about aggrandizing the mansion, and some of the original squires felt obliged to keep up; in part, because of the new fashion for hygiene, which involved pipes. Very few of the older manors would have stood up to having holes knocked in them for pipes, so their owners started from scratch and put up new houses.

That, at any rate was what my grandfather had done, but why he had wanted such a large one, nobody knew. He was a retiring, not an ostentatious, man. Perhaps his wife had insisted—the Irish were famous for their dreams of palaces and kings and glory—or perhaps he had merely got into the hands of a powerful architect. The only features of the house he had insisted on designing himself were the fire escapes. Fires were his hobby; as a young man his greatest treat had been to join the local fire brigade on one of their practices, and he was said to have set up a record for celerity in donning his uniform, sliding down the pole and taking up action stations on the horse-drawn fire machine.

So, in the early 1890s, the old Boscombe was demolished and a lavish new one begun. Little entertaining was done at Boscombe, life was simple and took place mainly out of doors, so something scarcely more elaborate than an early British shelter would have done. However, there it was; up went the brave new Boscombe until, about three-quarters of the way through, disaster struck. The workmen were dismissed, the horses and carriages sold, gardeners laid off; everything came to a halt, and the family moved into a semi-derelict rectory they rented for £30 a year, rates included.

The seed of this disaster had been sown in my grandfather's undergraduate days at Cambridge. There he had not, we understood, been numbered among the "bloods", but in his college there was a set of much richer and more dashing scholars who gambled heavily. One of these young men had persuaded my grandfather to back some kind of I.O.U. for £100,000. My grandfather must have been mad to do this, and realized his mistake a few days later. He brought himself to tell his fellow undergraduate that he had made a promise he would be unable to keep, since he did not possess £100,000 or anything like it. The young man, whom we will call Lord Snapdragon, laughed the matter off, and said that everyone had drunk too much brandy, and anyway he had won it all back again next day. He promised to destroy the document; and my grandfather thought no more of it for over thirty years.

After leaving Cambridge my grandfather had disappeared for two years, returning with a bushy black beard, one or two ferocious scars, and tales of life among the Iroquois, more or less on the site of what was to become Chicago. After that he went to China, then into Parliament, and finally inherited Boscombe, where he settled down to raise his family, fulfil his civic duties, stand for Parliament and tend his estate, helping whenever possible to put out fires, establishing plantations, and walking everywhere about his property in gaiters, breeches and a brown billycock hat.

Lord Snapdragon pursued a more chequered career. He progressed through several fortunes to end, inevitably, in the bankruptcy court. The only surprising thing was that he managed to ward it off for so long. Then there arrived at Boscombe a letter to say that the I.O.U., or whatever it was, bearing my grandfather's signature, had been produced and, with regrets, was presented for immediate settlement.

Lord Snapdragon's creditors, I have always thought, must have been bluffing. To begin with, my grandfather had been a minor at the time; over thirty years had gone by, I do not suppose the document had been properly witnessed, and it seems most unlikely that any court of law would have upheld it. Had my grandfather contested it, probably the whole matter would have been dropped. Seeing that he had a wife, five children and an enormously costly three-quarters-built house on his hands, this appeared to most people to be the prudent and, indeed the proper course to take. "It is a debt of honour," my grandfather said. In his view that settled the matter—except how to find £100,000, which presented considerable difficulties. These he solved by insuring his life for, we always understood, the largest sum ever known, up until then, on a single individual, and said to involve a premium of £10,000 a year. He raised £100,000 on the policy, handed it over to the creditors of Lord Snapdragon (who went bankrupt a second time a few years later) resigned his Parliamentary seat and faced the world, with his dismayed family, completely penniless. Boscombe's rent-roll almost exactly covered the premium on the policy. My grandmother had swooned, and been conveyed from her sofa to an Irish packet and thence to her childhood home in County Meath, accompanied by her two younger children. The older ones went to the derelict rectory with an old nanny and several under-maids. Destitute as the family was, penniless and all but starving, a small retinue accompanied them into exile; but all the menservants were dismissed, and the more expensive women like the housekeeper and cook and senior housemaids.

It was a *debâcle*. Only my grandfather kept his equilibrium and his spirits, and set about looking for a job.

At over fifty, with little experience beyond that of estate management, pruning young trees, fighting fires and a rusty knowledge of the Iroquois tongue, this cannot have been easy. But luckily, in that bygone world, provided that you kept your honour, you did not lose your friends. No one could have called my grandfather's behaviour anything but honourable. In a very short time, he had been found some position in the City, in which he displayed a great deal more acumen than anyone had expected. Before long he found himself a director of several important companies, including one of the railways, which provided him not only with a substantial fee but with a small golden key he wore upon his watchchain, and which entitled him and any lady of his choice to free accommodation in a *de luxe* coach on any railway not merely in Britain, but in any European country except Russia; and later on he took his daughters on several highly enjoyable excursions to places like Baden-Baden and Homburg. All this would not have happened if he had not backed Lord Snapdragon's I.O.U. and then met his debt, so perhaps a somewhat quixotic idea of honour paid off in the end. But he never lived again at Boscombe. When he died, Rufus was able to inherit unencumbered by debt, and the uncompleted condition of the top floor made games of "fox" all the more exciting.

Chapter Seven

EVERY Christmas, Lilli gave a party for the village children and put on a play. This gave her an excuse to invite to Boscombe a *posse* of her own relations, who practically drove Rufus from the house. Joy remained his *bête noire*. Her political idols were Ramsay MacDonald, Philip Snowden and other Labour leaders whose very mention raised my uncle's blood pressure; and she declaimed with equal vehemence against Mr. Stanley Baldwin, who was in the pay of the Americans. "He wears a nightshirt and a sleeping cap," she added. "I have it on the best authority."

Then there was a withered Russian countess: dictatorial, incomprehensible and boring, she tottered about with a stick, followed by a horrible parrot which dashed at peoples' ankles and bit them savagely, while the countess cackled with laughter; when it was not doing that, it sat on the pelmets and glared down ferociously with a red, beady eye, planning its next attack, or made messes all over the carpet. Miss Harriet, the countess called it; though I am sure it was a male. It especially hated Rufus, and would fling itself on his ankles with a flurry of feathers and screeches of rage; he once pursued it round the room trying to kick it, while Lilli crouched in a chair clasping her head and crying: "Rufus! Rufus, how *can* you, you brute, you beast, you murderer! Tormenting that poor defenceless bird! Devil, sadist, torturer, one day you'll pay for this!" She could not say "God will punish you" because she was an atheist, but the countess wailed and screeched to this effect, threw a fit of hysterics, and had to be revived with brandy. Rufus, his face a mottled purple, strode from the room without a word and did not re-appear for two days.

The nieces and nephews were not quite so bad. There was Sybil, dark and ivory-skinned with thick hair trimmed into an Eton crop, self-confident and lively and, like her mother, opinionated; there was Rudi, dreamy and musical and still at school—not at Eton, Winchester or Rugby, or even somewhere like Malvern or Uppingham, but in Switzerland; and there was grown-up Oliver, who had recently been called to the Bar. He was good-looking in a somewhat drooping way; his auburn hair had more than a suspicion of a wave, his skin was fine and pale, his nails were polished and his trousers very wide: this was the era of Oxford bags, that could look almost like skirts if carried to extremes. He had lived in Leipzig for a year, and sang German songs. A barrister's profession must be an exciting one, I supposed, defending murderers at the Old Bailey, or adulterers in scandalous divorces; but Oliver quickly dismissed these ideas.

"No money on the criminal side."

"Then which sides do pay?"

"Company law. I mean to make a packet before I'm forty and then go into politics."

"In which party?"

"I don't know yet. Depends on how the land lies in fifteen years' time."

Most of Lilli's relations were like that: they knew what they wanted, they knew their own minds. Lilli must have wanted Rufus once. I wondered why.

"His position, of course," Aunt Madge said.

"I shouldn't have thought Aunt Lilli would have envied that. Her family are all rich, and seem to have positions of their own."

"*Positions*? Those Bauers? A pack of jumped-up adventurers!"

To me, that made them all the more interesting, but Uncle Jack said: "I wouldn't trust one of them as far as the end of my nose. Bounders, every man-jack." "What's a bounder?" "If you don't know that, you don't know anything."

A big Christmas tree was set up in the Boscombe drawing room. It shone with real candles, each one wearing a little fuzzy halo of light, and looked magical instead of artificial, as a tree must look with modern electric bulbs in different colours; these had the soft gold of natural candle-light. On Christmas Eve presents for every child, forty or fifty of them, were tied to the branches with coloured ribbons. These Lilli had chosen individually at Hamley's or the Army and Navy Stores, which supplied, for older boys, wonderful pocket knives, each with two blades, a corkscrew, a gimlet and a prong for removing stones from horses' hooves; and, for the girls, hussifs, purses or neat little manicure sets. Each child had a bag of sweets as well. Presents for the family, the guests and all the domestics were heaped around the foot of the tree. Lilli must have bought literally hundreds of different things, and needed all her £2,000 a year and more to be so generous; the sad thing was that she no longer had it, nearly all her capital having been invested in Russian funds which disappeared in 1917. So it was Rufus who paid.

The children were conducted first to see the tree, glowing in total darkness except for the candles; then to the play in the ballroom, which had a mock minstrels' gallery and an organ loft; then to tea spread in the dining room, and, finally, to the plundering of the tree. This was a tricky operation, since the children were apt to set themselves alight. One year there had been a near-disaster, so now each child was allotted one candle to blow out, then the lights were switched on and presents claimed. By then the children were so replete they were fairly lethargic; one or two were generally sick. Lilli darted about amongst them clad in something chiffony and wearing diamonds and emeralds, instead of in the regulation country house tweeds, and looking exactly like a fairy queen. The whole thing must have made a lot of children believe in fairies. Rufus would have made an excellent ogre, but kept out of the way.

Christmas Day was devoted first to eating and then, in order to work off lunch and make room for dinner, to a paper-chase. This was the province of my cousin Ralph, and boycotted by the Bauer faction, who preferred to lie back in the drawing-room listening to classical records. "Bloody lot of milksops," Uncle Rufus said. I envied the milksops, but did not have the courage to join them, and, muffled in sweaters and a mac and wearing heavy brogue shoes, went reluctantly forth into the cold, wet drizzle. Ralph and one of the stable-boys went ahead with sacks of torn-up paper, and we knew we would have to trot and trudge for miles, probably to the top of Kingscliffe and back. Kate came with equal reluctance, but Gertrude stayed behind in the nice warm drawing room with the classical records and the Bauers. "She told Uncle Rufus she had the curse," Kate said. "What, not just like that!" "No, that she was feeling off-colour. Everyone knows what that means."

"As a matter of fact," Kate added, "only don't say I said so, I think she's got a crush on Oliver."

"Gert has? Not she!"

"Why not? He's quite attractive."

"In a way. Not her way, though. He's not . . ."

This was hard to put into words. He was not in a smart regiment, he had not been to the right school, his name was not to be found in Burke's or Debrett's; I suppose I was trying to say that Gertrude was a snob and cultivated only snob-worthy young men. This was true, but not the whole truth; after so much tossing about on the billows of temperament, uncertainty and poverty, she sought a reliable, well-found, comfortable and properly conducted vessel in which she could repose her confidence, and get as far away as possible from Nathan's Orchard. So I did not see her allowing herself to fall in love with a young man who could offer no security, and was as much of an opportunist as she was herself. But, of course, what you intend to do and what actually happens are two different, and as a rule quite opposite, things.

It was hard to believe that Ralph was Lilli's son as well as Rufus's, so faithfully did he follow his father. Physically, he was smaller, finer-boned and more graceful than Rufus, and this contribution of Lilli's had, ironically, increased his prowess in the field of sport she so despised. Ralph was outstandingly successful in any sport or game he took up. At Eton he won cups for boxing and athletics, he rode in the Grand National while still an undergraduate at Magdalen, he took part with distinction in ocean races, he got a pilot's licence; he was said by the *Daily Express* to have started the fashion for wearing polonecked sweaters. He was possibly an even better horseman than his father, and won innumerable point-to-points.

But Ralph was not dour like Rufus, he had a sense of humour and a lot of charm. Lilli spoilt him outrageously and when he was at Eton had sent him so many hampers of cold partridges, smoked salmon and game pies, that his friends had called him "Grubby", after the grub; in spite of this, he had retained his natural toughness, modesty and sense of proportion. He was easy to get on with, but his interests at this time were concentrated on horses, yachts and aeroplanes, and on the records set

6

up by the young men in charge of them. If he was interested in girls, he kept this dark. They had to be good sports, or nothing. He was a member of the Bullingdon club.

Ralph and the stable-boy were given fifteen minutes start with their sacks of torn-up paper and then off we pounded at a jog-trot across sodden pastures, over blackthorn hedges that ripped to shreds our stockings, through gateways where we sunk into black, viscous mud, and thence into a dark, dripping plantation with ruts deep in water, trodden into a quagmire by the hunt, where we lost the trail. The quarry was permitted, now and then, to trick us by such devices as going back on its tracks, and then we had to cast about like hounds until we found the line.

"I don't see how anyone can hope to catch Ralph," I said.

"Only by superior cunning."

"But our cunning isn't superior."

"Well, this is a damned silly way to spend an afternoon," Kate concluded. "They're bound to work back to Boscombe, aren't they? If we cut across and wait somewhere near Hiscocks', we might spot them coming back."

"Wouldn't that be cheating?"

Kate laughed. "It's not cheating if we use superior cunning. Anyway who cares if it is? We can get some tea off Mrs. Hiscock and dry our feet."

By now the chasers had picked up the line and were pounding doggedly through a waste of matted bracken on the slopes of Kingscliffe. We let them go. At the Hiscocks' it was milking time. Mr. Hiscock and two sons were in the shed sending jets of milk frothing into buckets held between their knees. Each milker rested his buttocks on his three-legged wooden stool and pressed his forehead into the soft, elastic flank of a munching cow. Hurricane lamps with smoky glasses depended from a forest of rafters receding into the darkness of the tiled roof; cobwebs hung down in long, coagulated strips like ectoplasm. There was a soothing symphony compounded of munch-munch, the rattle of chains, the hissing of milk into buckets, the flop-flop of falling dung; and a delicious, immemorial smell compounded of ripe hay, linseed, fresh dung, ancient grime, swedes, sweet steamy bovine breath and supple bovine flesh and goodness knows what else. The cows were of all shapes and colours. One or two shiny-coated calves, roped by their necks to a stanchion, bleated now and then, waving agitated tails. A man with boots thick as boards, his corduroy trousers tied under the knee, clumped in with two wooden buckets supported by a yoke across his shoulders, bringing water to the cows. When a milking bucket was full, the Hiscocks tipped its contents into a separator standing in the dairy next door, and swung the handle, and skim milk gushed, while cream trickled, out of two different nozzles.

As it was Christmas Day, Mrs. Hiscock was not, for once, baking or roasting at her enormous range that occupied the whole of one end of the kitchen; they had eaten their dinner— always roast beef at Christmas—and she was mending a pile of thick woollen socks before the men came in for tea, which was already spread on the table. The amount English people ate never ceased to astonish me. Mrs. Hiscock prepared three square meals a day—very square ones—for herself and Mr. Hiscock, two surviving sons—the two eldest had been killed in the war— and two smaller children, plus a mother-in-law crippled with rheumatism and two hired men whom they boarded. There was also a simple-witted niece, who helped; three or four dogs, several cats, a canary, and, in their season, a quantity of lambs being raised on the bottle. The larder, as big as the parlour, was full of jams, preserves, chutneys and pickles, and salted string beans, and jars of lard rendered down from the last pig, and wide-mouthed earthenware crocks full of eggs in isinglass, and, under the shelves on the stone-flagged, uneven floor, casks of elderberry, dandelion and parsnip wine. Sides of home-cured bacon hung from a kitchen beam and in a corner was a sack of feathers; they had killed a goose, and Mrs. Hiscock was going to stuff a pillow.

She clucked over our water-logged condition and, as the men were still absent, we took off our skirts as well as our shoes and what was left of our stockings, and hung them over chairs in front of the kitchen range.

Mrs. Hiscock pressed upon us food we did not want.

"Seeing as it's Christmas, a drop of parsnip wine wouldn't do any harm."

It did good. We had a splendid gossip. Like practically every-one else on the place, Mrs. Hiscock had been in service at Boscombe, and remembered it in the time of its glory. Christmas Day was a good occasion to recall the past. Mrs. Hiscock's first year's pay she told us,—she was fourteen—had been six pounds without the uniform but everything found, and a good table. Hard work but you expected that with all the stairs, the coals, the hip-baths in bedrooms, polishing grates, and the strictness of the housekeeper who was hooked into black bombazine. She and Wigmore, the butler, were co-deities of that enclosed world, and ate alone together, apart from the others unless there was a visiting valet to entertain or a ladies' maid, some-times French. Never a dull moment, Mrs. Hiscock said, at least in retrospect, with the young footmen fancying themselves in striped waistcoats and shiny buttons, and the coachmen in cockaded hats, and once a year a servants' ball that went on until five in the morning and provided conversation for months.

When Boscombe closed, this community disintegrated. Mrs. Hiscock stayed at home to mind an ailing mother and to stitch leather gloves farmed out by a factory in Yeovil—sixpence a pair, she got, provided they were perfect. "One stitch just the least little bit uneven, out they went and you got nothing," she said. "But they was good gloves." She and Ernest Hiscock were courting for ten years. His father was a tenant, and tenancies normally descended from father to son; when this one came to Ernest, they wed.

"Seeing as it's Christmas, another drop of parsnip wine wouldn't do any harm."

By the time the men got in from milking we had consumed quite a few drops, and had a fit of giggles getting back into our skirts. The men parked their lanterns in the porch and filed in silently, smelling of cowshed. Kate began to recite verse.

> "Shades of night were falling fast
> As through an Alpine village passed——"

A hiccup interrupted her, so I continued:

"A youth who bore mid snow and ice
A banner with a strange device———"

Our joint "Excelsior!" must have rung raucously in the ears
of the gentle Hiscocks and their lodgers who, washed and un-
booted, awaited their tea. The kitchen had become full of large,
slow-moving, pink-faced men in corduroys, with big hands,
standing quietly like the cows they had just left munching in the
shed.

"Best run them back in the trap, Dad," Mrs. Hiscock
suggested.

The Hiscocks' trap was drawn by a lively roan called Bricks
that Mr. Hiscock hired out for hunting at ten shillings a day;
but if there were no customers, he sometimes lent the pony to
one of my cousins. Before we reached Boscombe, Mr. Hiscock
had promised him to me next day. Kate would have to ride the
fat Buttercup, an inferior mount, but she was too tiddly to mind,
and burst into snatches of song all the way home. Bricks's hooves
went clip-clop, clip-clop, clip-clop on the macadam, the trap's
springs creaked, the carriage lantern, secured to its bracket by
an iron spike, threw long shadows that leapt about the hedges
and black ditches as if a demented spirit was dancing attendance
on us. The parsnip wine glowed inside, and we sang "Tie a
String Around Your Finger," and "Tea for Two."

"What on earth are we going to say?" I wondered.

"Oh, we'll think of something." Kate had little trouble in this
direction. "Aunt Lilli won't mind." But Uncle Rufus might—
not so much the parsnip wine as defection from the paper-chase.
Those who set their feet to paper-chases should finish them,
unless they fell out for some honourable reason like a broken
leg.

We need not have worried; no one had noticed our absence.
The paper-chasers had returned wet as otters but full of
triumph; needless to say, no one had caught up with Ralph.
After a hot bath, everyone tucked into a substantial tea which
staved off the pangs of hunger until the gong summoned us to
an enormous cold supper.

The Bauers displayed a very poor appetite, and no wonder,
cooped up all the afternoon indoors before a fire, smoking
scented cigarettes and playing records—decadent was the only

word. Gertrude was sleek as a pussy, with every hair in place and shining eyes. She was finding plenty to say to Oliver, who looked languidly attractive in a supercilious way. "You might be right," I remarked to Kate. "I'm always right, coz. You'll see."

Chapter Eight

THE Boxing Day meet was always held on the lawn at Boscombe, and everyone had cherry brandy. This was my first English hunt, and my main objective was to keep out of everyone's way. There were a lot of people to be avoided, mostly on enormous horses of savage mien who flattened their ears and were not above a vicious kick if jostled. Their riders also looked large and savage, with frosty if not actually vicious expressions, and were swathed in thick, heavy clothing: great big boots, long-skirted coats or stiff habits, necks bandaged into white stocks, heads supporting hard-brimmed top-hats or bowlers. After the simpler, more casual hunts of Africa, with people in open-necked shirts and old jodhpurs or trousers mounted on small, untrimmed ponies, it all looked very ritualized and alarming, like the observance of some fierce religious cult, derived perhaps from Druids and also centred on a blood sacrifice. Kate and I rode astride and wore breeches, which put us into the childrens' category.

Mr. Hiscock was as good as his word and one of his sons brought Bricks to the meet for me to ride, free of charge. The hounds surged about the Boscombe lawns like a restless brown-and-white-wave, clumsy, good-natured and stupid, thrusting slobbery muzzles into everything and perpetually wagging their tails. I knew this was the wrong way to describe their actions; their tails were sterns, just as those of foxes were brushes. I had a nodding acquaintance, if no more, with the fox-hunting tongue, derived mainly from the works of Surtees (that most under-rated of English social satirists), from a large red book given me for my fourteenth birthday called *The Sport of Our Ancestors*, and from our (so to say) home-made African hunts across the *veld* in pursuit of anything from jackal to giraffe, steinbock to warthog. (A warthog's tail could scarcely be a brush?) As in any faith, even among the initiates there were different usages. Some fox-hunters talked about pink coats, and regarded anyone who spoke of a red one as an ignoramus; at

Boscombe, to talk about a pink coat was to commit a serious solecism; coats were red, and that was that. I often wondered why anyone should call them pink when they were scarlet, and did not find out for years that it was because the first ones were made by a Mr. Pink, a tailor. Like tartan kilts and Christmas trees, scarlet coats were a nineteenth-century invention; John Peel's coat had been grey, not gay.

Ralph came up and said: "They're drawing Faggots first; if you nip down behind Prideaux's buildings and round Parsons' plough-ground you'll be well placed if they go away towards Adders' Reach as they generally do." It was kind of Ralph to take such trouble over two scruffy, insignificant cousins; he was a kind young man. His mount was an enormous, fierce looking steed, no doubt straight from the Irish bogs, that would obviously jump a haystack if asked. Ralph, with his healthy fresh complexion and merry brown eye, looked extremely smart and handsome; he rode, as the saying goes, as if born in the saddle, which certainly would not have been the case with any *accouchement* of Lilli's.

She took no part in the hunt or its preliminaries, and in an ostentatious manner, boycotting the whole affair. Soon after she had come to Boscombe, she had removed all the stuffed foxes' heads (masks, I know) from the walls and thrown them on a bonfire. Rufus had turned as mottled as a turkey-cock; each one enshrined a cherished memory; when she had replaced them by Japanese prints and Chinese scrolls, he had been forced to avert his eyes. Finally, she had gone too far; a massive figure of the Buddha was installed in place of a marble bust of Mr. Gladstone, and wafts of incense drifted about the house, even into the gunroom and Rufus's estate office where he spent much of his time. With bloodshot eyes and grunted oaths, muttering about heathen idols, pagan rites and blasphemous obscenities, he smashed the Buddha on the front-door-posts and kicked the fragments down the steps. Lilli threw a fit of hysterics, brought down curses on him for a sacrilegious vandal and a jackbooted Hun, and vanished for a week with her smelling salts, ladies' maid and two Pekineses to her sister in London.

One up to Rufus: but Lilli had her revenge. The Prince of Wales came sometimes to the neighbourhood to hunt with the next-door pack, the Stanford Vale. Rufus despised this pack, and had a deep and bitter feud with its Master. The Prince's predilection for this unsporting outfit and its sodden, wire-infested country strained his loyalty almost to breaking point, but he managed to retain it by concluding that the Stanford Vale's Master had cast some kind of heathen spell over the future monarch.

There came a day when he received word of the Prince's intention to sample the sport offered by the Boscombe pack. This was a tremendous challenge. To show not merely better sport, but sport of a wholly different order from anything the Stanford Vale could rise to, became a matter of life and death.

That Rufus was a sportsman to the core went without saying. He would rather have been torn to pieces like one of the foxes he hunted than break the least of the rules. So, despite the over-riding importance of showing good sport, there was little he could do to ensure it. The Prince must take his chance with wind and weather, the whims of foxes and the moods of hounds. Nevertheless certain hunts, to overcome such hazards, had been known to resort to a "bag fox"—one caught and shut up in a stable or kennel until wanted, and then released some half-hour before the meet. All true fox-hunters looked askance at this unsporting practice. Nevertheless it was done, probably more often than was generally admitted. Rufus was tempted, just this once. A bag fox, after all, was a wild one, the chase itself was genuine, and was it not his loyal duty to give satisfaction to the heir to the throne?

So, under conditions of maximum security, a fox was caught and concealed in the stables. Everyone involved was sworn to secrecy, the stable was locked, the kennelmen instructed to stay away from the pub. How Lilli ferreted out the secret, no one ever discovered. Only the huntsman, the head gamekeeper and one of the kennelmen were in the know and their loyalty was unquestioned. Lilli did sometimes tour the stables bearing lumps of sugar for the horses, and perhaps a locked loose-box had aroused her curiosity. At any rate, on the morning of the Prince's visit, this door was found open and the fox gone.

Rufus came in to breakfast black as thunder and stampeded round the house like an affronted bull, cross-questioning everyone. He did not cross-question Lilli; she came downstairs, as usual beautiful and tiny and perfectly turned out, and smelling of lilies of the valley, laughing openly. "So your little trick hasn't worked, Rufus?" she tinkled at him. "*What* a shame! Never mind, it'll make a splendid story. You'll have the satisfaction of knowing you've supplied the locals with a good laugh." Goodness knows why he never really did become a murderer. He must have had more self-control than we imagined. Poor Rufus, the great day turned into a disaster; the scent was bad, the hounds kept changing foxes, one of which ran to ground in a drain, the Prince had two falls, and of course in no time the story of the bag fox was all over the Stanford Vale.

Ralph steered a skilful course among these domestic reefs and tempests. He was on his father's side in the essentials, but in thrall to his mother's beauty and charm. Rufus kept him on a strict allowance, but he was never short of cash. "You won't be content," Rufus said bitterly, "until you've ruined that boy's character." Following on the grub at Eton, Lilli kept her son supplied with expensive silk dressing-gowns, ivory-backed hairbrushes, gold cigarette cases and skin lotions from Paris that his father would have smashed like the Buddha if he had discovered them; but Ralph used them only to please Lilli now and again. Miraculously, he remained more or less unspoilt.

"Where are the Bauer cousins?" I asked Kate at the meet.

"I don't suppose they've woken up yet. Unless they're reading Michael Arlen in bed."

"Lucky them."

"He came to the studio the other day," Kate added. "Michael Arlen I mean. Masses of black curls and big round eyes like an owl's and soft white hands, and a floppy silk tie and a tiny monkey sitting on his shoulder. Such a *sad* smile. He talked about Mexico and human sacrifices. His cigarettes smelt funny, I expect they were doped."

From the point of view of dedicated sportsmen, the Boxing Day meet was a chaotic occasion. All sorts of people turned up on foot, on bicycles, in pony-carts and occasionally in cars, though this was frowned on and in any case was futile, since lanes were too narrow to turn in, and cars always stuck in gateways. Bicycles were all right, but most of the general public followed on foot and of course got in the way, and often caused the fox to change course. Children on fat, stodgy ponies like Buttercup cluttered the gateways and fell off at inconvenient places, and people's Christmas guests appeared on hired cobs. Regulars resigned themselves to poor day's sport compensated for by humorous incidents like people falling off in brooks, getting lost and calling down lurid oaths from members of the priesthood like Rufus. It was a trying day for Rufus altogether and we were more than ever resolved to keep out of his way.

"Did you *really* meet Michael Arlen?" I inquired of Kate as we made our way in the direction Ralph had suggested. I was impressed; his books were all the rage, though I preferred Ronald Firbank and James Branch Cabell.

"One of my friends at the studio goes to Paris with him for week-ends. He takes her to an extraordinary nightclub with a glass floor where you can watch goings-on between women and donkeys."

"*Donkeys?* Surely they'd . . ." Bricks disrupted this unexpected train of thought by shying and nearly throwing me into Parsons' plough-ground, where water glistened in furrows that ran straight as railway lines. I had not yet got used to the wonderful evenness of these English furrows; at home, a ploughed field was all lumps and tussocks. Nor to the way every inch was cultivated: the English plough turned a furrow right into the hedge, and finally the ploughman dug out the corners with a spade and threw seed-corn into them by hand. Land was so precious. And I marvelled at the big, heavy, patient horses drawing a single-furrow plough, followed by a silent plodding man in gaiters, and a cloud of white gulls wheeling and swooping. At home we had teams of twelve or even sixteen oxen, and barefoot drivers clad in blankets cracking long whips and shouting at the bullocks.

Kate and I took up our position where Ralph had suggested, beside an untarred lane. Buttercup settled down to nibble at the bank. We heard the horn tu-tu-tu-ing in the distance, coming nearer; the hunt had moved off, and in our direction.

"I didn't see Tony at the meet," I said.

"I think he's come unstuck."

"I'm not sure he was stuck in the first place."

"Well, Nathan's Orchard takes a bit of getting used to. Gertie could have landed Geoffrey if it hadn't been for the bailiffs."

"That was before I came."

"He was rather sweet, with a little fair moustache and a kind of wistful look and a father with a large estate in Somerset, or it may have been Dorset. Anyway there he was, gawping at Gert with his mouth open, you know—she had him cold. But sooner or later the time comes when she can't keep her young men away from Nathan's Orchard any longer."

"Yes, but I should think it might strike them as a place to rescue Gert from."

"Like the jaws of death you mean? I daresay it might, but Geoffrey was unlucky, he found the bailiffs in."

"What do bailiffs do when they're in?"

"These sat about all over the drawing room with their hats on, smoking cigars someone had sent daddy for his birthday, playing cards. It wasn't exactly the best moment for a suitor."

"But where was Uncle Jack?"

"He'd got word somehow or other and cleared out. I don't know where to."

"With Aunt Madge?"

"No, she'd taken Bergamot to Sir Lewis because she had a tumour, Bergamot I mean. He's a sort of super-vet in London who charges fifty guineas I believe. So when the bailiffs came, there was only Gert. Geoffrey turned up unexpectedly and of course it was the end of *him*."

"Poor Gert."

"She cried for two days."

All of a sudden, the straggly wood and gorse brakes became alive. The hounds were seething about, sterns waving like storm-tossed boughs, uttering now and then a yelp or gruffer cry. Men were yoiking and lew-in-ing and cracking whips amid a jingling of bits and squelching of hooves. Horses thudded along the lane or crashed about in the undergrowth. It was a noisy thing, the hunt. To mingle with the gentle scents of winter earth, moist and ripened; of spongy moss, of rotting timbers, of moulds and fungi and the sleeping roots, came fresh and sharper smells of wet leather, equine sweat, dogginess and horse-droppings that plopped on to the lane and steamed in misty air. All at once there was another smell: the sharp, acrid whiff of fox, and a flash of russet as he slipped across the lane and streaked across a pasture. The air fairly split with screams and holloas, with a cracking of whips and tu-tu-tu-ing of the horn. Bricks quivered and tensed, but Buttercup went on nibbling at the bank. Kate and I had taken refuge in the ditch, while the hunters crowded through a nearby gateway.

"We'd better wait till they——" Kate began and got no farther. Enormous animals came towards us like charging buffaloes, tall as houses. The flaring nostrils, the huge muscled shoulders of Rufus's Irish heavyweight came thundering at me. I felt like a creature vainly fleeing from the Charge of the Light Brigade, except that there was nothing light about my uncle or his gigantic steed, and nowhere to flee to.

"Look out——"

Kate and I flattened ourselves against our ponies' necks at the same instant, thereby probably saving our lives. "Our brains," Kate subsequently remarked, "if any, would have been strewn all over the bank." I felt the brush of air as hooves passed over with an inch to spare. There was a crash as the horse landed on the far side of the bank, a gruff oath from his rider and then they were gone. For a moment we were silent.

"The old beast," Kate said shakily. "He went clean over us."

"Perhaps he didn't notice us."

"I'm going home."

We did not do so, however, but joined the throng shoving through the gateway. A young farmer in a rat-catcher's coat touched his bowler: this was Herbert Hiscock on a wild, rangy-looking horse he was training to participate in point-to-points.

"Near shave," he remarked in his warm burr. "The Master'd leap the devil himself if he was in the road."

"I could do with a barrelful of your mother's parsnip wine," Kate remarked. Herbert grinned. "I've a flask of port wine to keep the cold out later if 'eed like it."

In his shiny boots and white cravat, pink-faced and clean-shaven, Herbert looked quite different from when we had last seen him in his milking smock in the Hiscock kitchen: a nice, well-built young man, he was courting one of the three Miss Pickerings of Pound Farm. Their father was a kind of inventor; he had converted the stables into a little factory where milk was turned not only into powder and a precursor of processed cheese, but into objects like buttons and fountain pens and combs; he was very clever. The girls took part in this and were clever too and had been much better educated than we had; they could type and understand accounts, and did not lack suitors, but Mr. Pickering did not consider any of the local young men good enough for them.

Herbert touched his hat brim again and vanished, streaking across the field with the rest of the hunt. Bricks pounded after with pricked ears, full of enthusiasm. He knew the way much better than I did, and fat old Buttercup was soon left behind. We even jumped a hedge more or less successfully. The gate-ways were hock-deep in mud. A herd of young cattle stood bunched together in a corner of a field, staring in alarm, their collective breath steaming on the moist air. I was afraid Bricks was going to run away with me and charge some large obstacle like a gate, but he was a good-mannered animal. It was not his fault that I tumbled off into a ditch after he had slipped and fallen; we rolled about in icy water and viscous slime to emerge more or less indistinguishable from each other. I had managed to stick to rule one, instilled into me years ago; to hang on to the reins through thick and thin; but the saddle had slipped round and become a kind of undercarriage. Someone came along and helped me put it right and set forth again—one of the grooms, who was picking a way quietly in the rear on a relief mount.

"If you cut round by Tydings' past the Waggoners' Arms to the Mandeslip crossing you'll come up with them, I reckon," he advised. All this was double Dutch to me. Hunting in England, I was beginning to see, was a kind of mock warfare with every man his own general, anticipating the moves of the enemy and basing his success largely on a close, almost yard-by-yard knowledge of topography. There were plenty of short cuts. While to "go well" was admirable, so also was consideration for your steed, and the one could sometimes cancel out the other.

I decided to attach myself to the second horseman, who would doubtless know all the dodges. He was a taciturn fellow, with one of those lined, leathery faces horsemen so often display, and a hard, watery blue eye, and the yellow stub of a cigarette permanently between his thin lips; in some mysterious fashion the cigarette never seemed either to be replaced by a new one, or to come to an end and be discarded. Occasionally he would make remarks like: "turned him down by Snortings Tump I reckon," or: "they'll run him now to Oversandlesbury's End," making all these judgments by ear and instinct.

It had grown suddenly very quiet, and we seemed to be all alone under a grey sky among green pastures stretching away, one after the other, with now and again a field of roots, and young cattle and some melancholy sheep. Even the distant sounds of the hunt had faded. "Lost him down by Sodbury Thickets," my companion diagnosed. "If we cut past Handlebars we'll likely to find 'em." It sounded like Handlebars. We broke into a trot. My legs were aching and I was getting a blister on my seat, and my feet felt like frozen codfish. This seemed to me a sad, unhealthy form of pleasure and I thought longingly of hot baths and scalding tea and boiled eggs, not to mention Herbert Hiscock's port, yet I did not want to give in and go home and feel, for absolutely no reason, in some way disgraced. Oliver, Sybil and Rudi certainly would not think such an action disgraceful, but as the most rudimentary form of common sense. They must be very snug, I thought, playing records in the library, with a roaring fire, and hot scones brought in by a parlour-maid with a silver teapot and jug.

"Are we far from Boscombe?"

My companion jerked his head. "Over past Junipers' Rise and Smedley Common. Matter of five miles." We were riding, I regretfully perceived, in the opposite direction. At last the silence was broken by a distant baying, and then the summons of the horn.

"Found in the gorse by Foggings quarry. They'll run to Blisteridge." He headed his horse in the direction of a small wood that straggled up a rise towards a bit of blue sky that had surprisingly appeared in the leaden canopy.

The sounds grew closer. We began to canter, and Bricks got excited again. Our path and that of the hunt were clearly about to converge. Soon we could see brown and white creatures racing across a field and then the horsemen, red or black, their headgear bobbing above their mud-bespattered, panting steeds.

"There he goes," said my companion. I could not see the fox, but knew the baying pack was gaining on him. Then came a subtle but distinct change of note, a deeper clamour and ferocity: they had changed from scent to view. Our horses quickened their speed without any urging; the hounds were in the next field and we were ahead of them, but they were veering towards the copse for which the fox was clearly making. He got as far as the edge of the gorse and no farther. By the time they pulled him down we were fifty yards away and had reined in our horses. The hounds surged over their bedraggled quarry and his end was swift. No doubt it was cruel, but so are most ends. Few foxes, probably, die peacefully in bed, hounds or no hounds. The pack surged like waves breaking over rocks, yelping and snarling, and then the scarlet coats were in amongst them as the hunt servants slid from their horses and waded in, screeching and yelling, with whips cracking. One of them managed to grab the limp, lacerated body and toss it up with a terrific caterwauling; it descended into the maw of the pack to be torn to shreds in an orgy of collective triumph.

I think the huntsman cut off the brush before he threw the body; at some stage, bits were collected and distributed as prizes by the Master to the most deserving followers. A select band of this élite, less than a dozen winnowed from the throng that had started off so boldly, had now drawn rein beside the gorse, and slid off their blown horses. Most of the riders, too, were blown, and like their horses still excited from the chase; they removed their hats and wiped their faces and exchanged remarks in loud voices, and looked round to see who was to be numbered among their blood-brothers. A couple of women were among the chosen, but not Gertrude. The groom had withdrawn into the background and I did not at first realize that my position among this small, hard-riding brotherhood was a false one, to say the least. I looked every bit as muddy as the rest, and up till now no one had noticed me, but there I was, in at the kill. A man nodded at me in a friendly way and made some remark

charged with approval; however odd my appearance, I was one
of the band. I fiddled with the girths partly to hide my genuine
blushes, partly to avoid Herbert Hiscock, who would know
quite well that neither Bricks nor his rider were likely to have
reached this position in an orthodox way.

"Five mile point, near enough," I heard Herbert say.
"Thought we'd lost him over by Hartlebury Turnpike." He
came over and offered his flask, one of those curved to fit a
breast pocket. "Drop of this instead of parsnip, eh? You've an
eye for the country, no mistake."

"Well, actually it was . . . I fell off and . . ." I had a swig at
the delicious port, got out my beef sandwiches and felt better.
Probably other people had taken short cuts, too. I patted Bricks's
wet shoulder gratefully, and he shook his head; probably his
thoughts were much like mine, of the homeward jog, the dry
stable, the rub-down and warm blanket and satisfying feed.

Rufus strode towards me with the purposeful determination
of a ritual priest. He looked enormous, all bone and gristle,
more than ever like a gorilla, with bloodshot eyes, and clasped a
bloody object in his hand. I shrank away, but here was no escape.

"You been blooded, huh?"

"Oh, yes, thank you, Uncle Rufus. Several times."

Rufus's face contorted; whether this was the birth of a smile,
a twinge of pain or just a habit I had no way of knowing. He
thrust the bloody object under my nose. "Here you are, then.
He was a good 'un." When I hesitated he added: "Come on,
Sybil." My hand closed on a cold, wet paw, hacked off at the
ankle.

"Oh, thank you, Uncle Rufus. Actually I'm not Sybil."

"You were yesterday." He strode off to distribute other bits
of cadaver, leaving me with my unearned trophy. Did you have a
paw mounted and hung on the wall? Or turned into some supposedly useful object, as elephants' feet were turned into
umbrella stands and buffaloes' hooves into inkwells? What could
a paw (a pad, correctly) become? The handle of a paper-knife?
Perhaps a brooch? It was large for a brooch, but all sorts of
unlikely objects could be pressed into the service of adornment;
in the war I had been sent a brooch made from a bit of brought-
down Zeppelin, and Maggie swore that a stone extracted from

7

one of her husbands' kidneys had become a cameo; this I was inclined to doubt, however.

Other followers were now arriving, with tales of hazard and mishap; after a short pause, people tightened girths and re-mounted, and the chase was resumed. It was early yet and, on a good day, Rufus reckoned to kill two or three foxes. It would be long past dark before he clattered into the stable yard.

Hacking to the meet and home again, however far and how-ever tired you and your horse might be, was all part of the game, and no mean part either. In these bucolic parts, horse-boxes were still frowned upon. In the morning came the early start after a lamplit breakfast; the sleek fresh horses neatly clipped, the start of a journey, it might be in keen frosty air with pale winter sunshine slanting on to ice-puddles and black hedgerows and silvery boles of trees; the narrow untarred lanes, huge flocks of starlings in the fields and the clapping of armies of pigeons. At the day's end came aching limbs and blisters, stiff wet reins, a stumbling steed, interminable miles on hard roads, a bitter wind piercing to the very marrow, pangs of hunger; and a feeling of willpower exercised and hardship mastered: a tiny, pale reflection of one of the labours of Hercules. All this led up to the delights of stripping off your wet clothes, a steaming bath, gulping hot tea and toast and a boiled egg by the fireside, tired limbs rested and a glow all over like a bather's after a cold plunge.

Of all this the horse-box deprived you, and of deeper things, so people like my uncle felt: sticking at it, and the naturalness of a country sport derived from the countryman's need to keep down foxes. Uncle Rufus saw the horse-box as a tool of forces that were sapping moral fibre, one more step along the road to national decadence, like the feasts, slaves, circuses and orgies that had undone imperial Rome. It was doubtful if horse-boxes and an Empire went together. There were no horse-boxes at Boscombe, where Rufus, that great hunter, like Barham, gloried and drank deep. The trucks and articulated lorries that thunder past his grave today cannot break his sleep.

Chapter Nine

OUR Bauer cousins, also, had enjoyed their day. They had sat about in the music room, discovered a rare Italian work in the library, read aloud some poetry, played the gramophone, walked to the village and back before lunch, eaten a large meal and talked interminably. Gertrude had turned up early in the afternoon saying that her horse had cast a shoe, and joined the non-hunters. Now she was looking very elegant in a short, straight frock of flame-coloured *crêpe-de-chine* trimmed with black lace, sitting on a sofa with Oliver.

"I hear you covered yourself with glory," she remarked to me, "and now you're Uncle Rufus's blue-eyed niece."

"I shouldn't think so for a moment. First of all he jumped clean over me as if I'd been a gate and then he mixed me up with Sybil."

"He did that on purpose to annoy you. He knows Sybil perfectly well, she put a frog in his chamber-pot."

"That wasn't her idea," Oliver said. They all stuck together and defended each other, quite unlike the cousins on our side of the family. He added: "I never thought it was a very good one."

"Where's Kate?" I inquired.

"I thought she was with you."

"Buttercup couldn't keep up."

"Then she must be lost."

"Ought someone to look for her?"

"I expect she'll turn up," Gertrude said.

No further interest was taken in Kate. For Gertrude, it was plain, there was no one in the room but Oliver. The gramophone, playing soft jazz, lured her from the sofa to practice Charleston steps on the thick carpet, ear-rings bobbing, her face animated: diamonds and honey. Oliver lounged back looking disengaged but watchful; secretly, perhaps he was appraising her. She asked him if he really wanted to go into politics.

"The nation needs a saviour."

"You can't save it without any money."

"It will need saving just as much in ten years' time."

"And then you'll be rich?"

"Rolling. Besides, there are short cuts."

"I wish I knew them," Gertrude said.

"But you do."

Gertrude stopped Charlestoning and looked at him half angrily, half quizzically, and with a half smile—and equivocal look. "What are you suggesting, Nol?"

"Fox, fox."

"I've no idea what you're driving at."

"Come off it, Gert. You practise what I preach. The Boscombe hunt isn't only after foxes."

Gertrude went pink and her eyes filled with angry tears. "I hate you, Nol," she said.

"Do you know who you remind me of? Edna Best in that awful play that's such a howling success."

"It's not an awful play. Everyone says it's marvellous."

"How could it be, with such a stupid title?" He was referring to *The Constant Nymph*. They started to bicker at least half in earnest, Gertrude determined to keep her temper and Oliver that she should lose it. At this game he could beat her hands down and she knew it; she half resented, half admired, his superiority.

"Slippery as an eel," she said later, being accustomed to less agile, meeker and more predictable fish who took the bait uncritically. "We've got some queer cousins." No doubt Oliver thought the same. I do not remember that he or Sybil ever came to Nathan's Orchard—wisely, indeed. They were not dog-lovers, and Aunt Madge referred to them as "those Jewish upstarts," although the Bauers were not Jewish, or if so very little, and some way back.

To Uncle Jack they were among "Lilli's filthy Reds". In his view Lilli was an arch-Red because she hero-worshipped Mr. Ramsay MacDonald and had once invited Sir Oswald Mosley to lunch. This was shortly after Mosley had deserted the Tories for the Independent Labour Party, whose members Rufus and his friends regarded as a bunch of cut-throats receiving orders almost hourly from the Kremlin, and bent on regicide, robbery and revolution. Labour politicians like Lansbury, Bevin and J. H. Thomas were one thing, but my uncle could not under-

stand how a man like Mosley, A Wykehamist who had been to
Sandhurst, had a splendid war record, a house in Smith Square
and had married Lady Cynthia Curzon, could become so base a
traitor as to join forces with revolutionaries like Fenner
Brockway, Jimmy Maxton and Kirkwood, or how Lilli could
lower herself to touch such very black pitch and not be defiled.

Affairs of state were, at this time, pretty safe in the hands of
Stanley Baldwin with his pipe, bowler and pigs in Worcester-
shire. Even Mr. Baldwin, however, somehow or other did not
command the full confidence of either of my uncles. He was not a
twister, certainly, like Lloyd George, but was he absolutely
sound? At least he had a sound Home Secretary in the shape of
Sir William Joynson-Hicks, who wore a frock coat and kept up
the traditions. Baldwin's money came from steel, not land.
Oliver despised him not merely for his middle-of-the-road
philosophy, but because he was a cousin of Rudyard Kipling's
and had praised inordinately the works of Mrs. Mary Webb.

"The act of a pander," Oliver said. "At least Lord Curzon
slept with Eleanor Glyn, he didn't drool over her literary style."
I felt crushed, having much enjoyed the works of Mrs. Webb.

Oliver praised writers we had either never heard of, like
Virginia Woolf and James Joyce, or heard of as immoral
bounders, like Hemingway and D. H. Lawrence. Now and again
Lilli, urged on by her nephew, would get one of their works
from Mudie's library, together with the more acceptable offer-
ings of such writers as Walpole, Bennett and E. C. Bentley. She
made great play of keeping them concealed from Rufus, who
might be expected to run amok if he so much as set eyes on their
jackets. In fact, it was unlikely that he would have paid them the
least attention, his literary interests being more or less confined
to *Horse and Hound*, manuals of kennel lore, stud records,
veterinary textbooks and Morley's *Life of Gladstone*.

When the first gong sounded and Lilli appeared, smelling
delicious as she always did, and walking as fastidiously as a
Persian cat, Kate's absence was remarked upon and for the first
time taken seriously. "We must ring up the police at once!"
Lilli exclaimed. "The child may be lying in a ditch with a broken
leg, or drowned in some dreadful torrent." "More likely to have
gone to the pictures in Otterbourne," Oliver remarked. Both

were wrong. Before the police could be called in, Kate appeared escorted by a slightly startled Wigmore and still in riding clothes on which the mud had congealed, walking unsteadily and clearly having trouble focusing her eyes. "Sorry t'be late Aunt Lilli, didn't know the time—no watch." She giggled. "Had a watch but it was popped. Popped." She giggled again, and it did sound funny, as a word you have never previously noticed can, on occasion, strike you as odd, or even hilarious. "Popped. Up the spout." The giggles spread, and shook us like a gust of wind. "Popped," Kate could hardly stand, what with the giggles and, as we rightly surmised, parsnip wine partaken at the Hiscocks', whither Buttercup had found her way.

"You'd better go to bed, my child," Lilli advised.

"Not tired. Hungry."

"What nunc will say if he sees you like this!"

"I am old, I am old, and my eyes are grown weaker, My beard is as white as the foam on the sea, Yet pass me the bottle and fill me a beaker, A bright brimming toast in a bumper for me," Kate unexpectedly quoted.

"I think it has brimmed enough already," Lilli observed.

The old countess made an entrance with Miss Harriet on her shoulder; that horrid bird ruffled its feathers, directed its ferocious glare at Kate, swooped to the floor and made a dash at Gertrude's ankles. "Keep away, you revolting bird," Gertrude implored. "Oliver, can't you save me?" "Birds are really reptiles," Oliver said, remaining seated. "But reptiles have nicer natures." The countess bent her ancient form in an endeavour to attract her pet's attention. "My poor Harriet, how you are suffering! She has constipation, all the morning she was with difficulty, and then there came only just one small pellet like a pea."

"What is time? The effluxion of life zoophitic In dreary pursuit of position or gain. What is life? The absorption of vapours mephitic And the bursting of sunlight on senses and brain! Such a life——"

"My child, if you're coming in to dinner you must fly and change. Hurry, hurry, hurry! Nunc will be with us any moment, the thunder of the gong will resound, away, away!"

"In thirty bright minutes from Ranksboro' Gorse." Kate

made her exit with dignity despite an ankle-rush by Miss Harriet; the door closed in the parrot's face just in time.

"Where did little Kate learn those improper words?" inquired the countess.

"They're not improper," Ralph said. "At least I don't suppose they are. It's a hunting ballad Kate recited at the last village concert. 'And when the run's over of earthly existence And you get safe to ground, you will fear no remorse, If you ride it, no matter what line or what distance, As straight as your fathers from Ranksboro' Gorse.' It went down awfully well. Usually they get *The Revenge* or old Gilpin."

"Fancy our little Ralph a poet! There should be a poem written for Miss Harriet and her feathers that are like jewels, as beautiful as the jewels of the Grand Duchess Anastasia when she——"

Lilli clapped her hands. "Come, come, children, we must be ready to keep your uncle entertained so that he won't notice dinner being late, while Kate changes. And you must all promise to *help* poor Kate and cover up any little lapses. I'll put her next to you, Oliver, will you look after her? We must keep the secret to ourselves! Sh, sh, not a word!"

A conspiratorial atmosphere enwrapped us, except for the countess, who inquired:

"What is all this? Has Kate been naughty?"

"She didn't mean to be."

"Ah! Those who mean to be, so seldom are. You do not slip if you are looking. My dear, if there should be *consequences*, you understand, there is an address in Paris——"

"No, no, that won't be necessary," Lilli said hastily. "Kate has not been as naughty as *that*. I expect we shall find her quite herself again in a few minutes. Where are my smelling salts?"

Rufus appeared in a benign humour; it had been a good day, he had bathed and shaved and changed into a claret-coloured smoking jacket and could look forward not only to an appetizing meal but to the imminent departure of all the Bauer relations, and Boscombe's return to its satisfactory routine.

Kate re-entered fairly steadily; the effects of the Hiscocks' hospitality were receding and had evidently bequeathed an afterglow. As we proceeded to the dining-room the parrot, with a blood-curdling shriek, charged the ankles of poor Wigmore, whose struggle to suppress beneath a butler-like decorum his instinct to kick the bird to blazes was reflected in a look of agony. He stood firm, and Miss Harriet, squawking with frustration, clambered up a curtain to the pelmet, where she screeched again and ejected a turd. "Get that bloody bird out of here," Rufus commanded, his face darkening. "Miss Harriet, Miss Harriet, stay where you are," cried Lilli. "The blood-lust is rising! Quickly Wigmore, the soup, the soup, and the soothing sherry . . ."

Apart from Rufus's after-dinner port, wine was served at Boscombe on special occasions only, and spirits never. Boxing Day was a special occasion. Wigmore went round with the decanter and missed out Kate, but Kate was in no mood to be passed over. "Just a sip, then," Lilli advised. "You must be careful." "I'm tired of being careful," Kate replied. "Come on, Wigmore, be a sport and fill it up." Wigmore registered disapproval, but, in response to a nod from Lilli, concurred. I was surprised that Lilli did not put her foot down. On the contrary she seemed to be, as it were, lifting it up, and encouraged Wigmore with a sign to fill Kate's glass when the champagne came round. He pursed his lips and did so, exuding disapproval, but Lilli merely winked at Oliver.

Kate grew garrulous but quite amusing, making scurrilous remarks about the goings-on at Miss Hapgood's, which sounded like an outpost of Montmartre in Bushey Park. When Wigmore missed her out again she swopped her empty glass for Oliver's full one. Lilli merely laughed indulgently. "Tomorrow we shall all disperse to toil and labour," she said with a tragic air. "Boscombe will be silent and deserted, no young voices, no shining faces, no laughter at the table; let us eat, drink and be merry while we may." When the glasses were again empty she cried: "A toast, a toast; there is a New Year coming, an old year dying, we must drink a toast to the brave New Year! More wine to drink the toast in, Wigmore, wine tasting of Flora and Provençal song and mirth, a beaded beaker full of the warm south—Wigmore, quickly, the blushful Hippocrene!" In the pause that followed, Kate's hiccup sounded loud and clear. She giggled, and everyone burst rather feverishly into conversation.

"The New Year approaches," Lilli cried. "Whose fortunes will be made or lost next year? Who'll be led to the altar. Which of my nieces and nephews will the darts smite?"

"Darts might," Kate said pensively, hiccupping again. "Darts might what? Let darts delight to bark and bite. Dart away, Fotheringay . . ."

"Hush, hush, my child, that will be enough." It was more than enough, and when Lilli rose to lead out the ladies, Kate's knees were unreliable, and her condition could no longer be concealed from Rufus.

"Is that girl tight?" he demanded. "Have I got a lot of drunken nieces as well as idle ones and ugly ones and ones with bloody manners?"

"Rufus, you monster! Little Kate just isn't feeling well— over-tired, poor child, from galloping about in all that mud all day with no nourishment! We'll soon have her safe in bed with some Ovaltine and a hot water bottle."

Kate was supported from the room and we all felt embarrassed; tiddly teenagers, in those days, were by no means to be taken in one's stride, especially in front of menservants; yet Lilli had egged her on. I felt quite at sea. In the morning, Kate remembered very little. "Did we have fireworks after dinner?" "No." "Funny. Something like that seemed to be going on. I feel sick." "I don't wonder."

We said goodbye to Lilli, who was reclining like a doll in a huge four-poster on a mass of pillows with embroidered slips, surrounded by books, newspapers, letters, smelling-salts, bottles of *eau de cologne* and lavender water, silver-topped cut-glass jars of creams and lotions, brushes and curling-tongs, all sorts of things. Her maid was in attendance, opening and shutting drawers and cupboards; much activity went on, with little visible outcome. Lilli's eyes looked enormous, so did the rings on her tiny fingers; she smelt like spring.

"My poor Kate, everything is forgiven and forgotten. Not a word will be said, this will be our secret."

"What will?"

"Dearest niece, your little, shall we say, indiscretion!"

"My eyeballs feel stiff, as if they wanted oiling. We haven't said goodbye to Uncle Rufus."

"Heavens, child, leave the lion undisturbed in his den! So far he's been very good, but we mustn't tempt providence. Be off now quickly and quietly, and later on I'll tell him that you couldn't find him to say goodbye."

The pony-cart was waiting in the stable yard with the faithful Buttercup, and Perce had come over to drive us back. Perce was a thickset, slow-spoken man with dark grey eyes, a ruddy complexion, and a shock of stiff hair; good-looking in a solid way. Solid yet not stolid; with all his brawn, he had about him a touch of something more volatile; perhaps he had a strain of gypsy blood. He was a Dorset man, and no fool; a deep one, people said.

He was a solitary, was Perce, a man without a family; he must have had one somewhere, but not all round him like everyone else. He lived in a basic little cottage on the farm and did for himself. With the men he was easy-going and they liked him, but were not wholly at ease; with Aunt Madge he was never less than civil, but at the same time perfectly firm. He agreed with what she said, and then did exactly what he had always intended. "Damn that Perce," she would grumble. "He's always got to know best." "No doubt he does," Uncle Jack pointed out. In her heart of hearts, Aunt Madge thought so too, and so while she would grumble at him, in the end she fell into line, and never went into one of her major sulks. If she had, he probably would not have noticed. There was something monumental about Perce; nothing could dent him. Something, too, of mystery. Had he feelings, hatreds and affections, ambitions, fears, hopes, failings? What did he think about in his solitary evenings? Had he ever been in love? No one knew. He never took a holiday. He kept ferrets, and went rabbiting on Sundays, and had a flutter on the horses now and then, and made a bit of money on the side castrating piglets; no one had a defter hand at this, the farmers said.

Gertrude, Kate, Perce and I filled the trap and weighed down the springs. There was an ancient rug, leather-lined and covered with horse-hairs, to pull over our knees; the air was cold and raw, the wind malicious, our string gloves were damp and our booted feet icy. When we reached the steep hill leading down into the vale, we got out and walked, lest our combined weight should be too much for Buttercup. We always had to walk up or down hills, as the case might be, to spare the pony, so it was only on the rare patches of flat ground that we were actually wheel-borne. Halfway down there was a stone trough, fed by a spring, for the refreshment of thirsty horses on their upward haul. It had been put there by our grandfather, who had sited benches for human plodders and troughs for equine ones at almost every bend of the road.

"Everything all right at home?" Gertrude inquired.

"Aye. Cowslip's had twins."

"Any dogfights?"

"Little tiff now and then."

"I know those little tiffs. Any casualties?"

Perce grinned. "Ears torn about a bit, that's all."

We presumed they were dogs' ears, not human ones.

Kate was wearing a fur jacket I had not seen before; rather tight for her, but it looked opulent and stylish. Gertrude observed it too.

"Where did that come from, Katie?"

"Aunt Lilli gave it to me."

"*Gave* it?"

"Of course. Why not?"

"She never mentioned it. Nor did you."

"It's one she's no further use for."

"Katie, I believe you pinched it!"

"Believe what you like," Kate said with dignity.

"She's bound to notice it's gone."

"She's got plenty of others."

"Katie! You'll end up in jail."

"I expect it's hereditary," Kate replied. She was referring to what was generally called, if mentioned, the family's skeleton, or sometimes poor Jack's lapse. When they married, Jack and Madge had possessed everything: looks, wealth, position, youth and *joie de vivre*. Too much *joie de vivre*, perhaps, and a liking for expensive forms of *joie*. They enjoyed themselves with hunters, carriages, hunting boxes, shoots in Scotland, chartered yachts, stunning dresses, jewelry, pretty well everything. Uncle Jack was madly in love.

Even in those days, certain military duties had to be

performed by young officers, who could not hunt four days a week in Leicestershire, slay birds and stags for months on end and go on yachting trips in the Mediterranean all the year round, although they could for most of it. There came a day when manœuvres on Salisbury Plain and grouse-shooting in Scotland clashed; Jack quitted the army to devote himself more whole-heartedly to sport and social life, and to stand for Parliament. The electorate speedily rejected him; tiresome tradesmen began to press for money, Jack had recourse to "the Jews", the net drew tighter. In the finish, Jack pawned some jewels that were not his to pawn, being on approval from a jeweller. The blow fell, the earth crumbled; the Judge delivered himself of a suitable homily about privilege, responsibility and besmirching the honour of an officer and gentleman, and for a couple of hours the raucous voices of newsboys at street corners shouted Uncle Jack's name.

It was a short sentence, and everyone was sympathetic; flowers poured into the house in Bruton Street, people left cards and came themselves in carriages. But Aunt Madge was having none of this. Disgraced, outcast, broken; the bitter fruit must be eaten down to the last pip. The more everyone tried to demonstrate that a little lapse such as this could happen to anyone and was no cause for undue sackcloth and ashes, the firmer became Madge's resolution to hang her head, tear her hair, heap on the ashes and sever herself from the society of decent folk. Disgraced, ruined and bankrupt as they were, Madge retained the services of several retainers, who were instructed to turn every caller from the door. She answered no letters, and invitations pressed upon her to stay in country houses were ignored. Aunt Madge prowled, as it were, around the banqueting halls into which she was bidden, looking for leper-holes and tolling a cardboard bell.

In due course the house in Bruton Street was sold and Madge retreated to Devon, where one of the farms on her father's property was fortunately vacant. Boscombe then stood empty; all this took place soon after the debâcle over Lord Snapdragon and the note of hand. The house at Nathan's Orchard was primitive and there was little money for improvements: enough to pipe water from a well to supersede the hand pump outside the back door, but not enough to install electricity. The roof was sound, however, if full of bees and starlings, and the land productive, if heavy and in need of drainage, with hedges overgrown, buildings dilapidated, gates falling to bits and pastures full of weeds.

So Uncle Jack was welcomed back from Wormwood Scrubs in the role of a farmer, one which he had never previously contemplated. To him, farmers were tenants who touched their caps and rode cobs. He tackled his new task in a military fashion, drawing up schemes, programmes and appreciations, and planning campaigns on maps. Aunt Madge donned the sackcloth almost literally—it was then that she adopted those shapeless black skirts covered with dog-hairs, and equally funereal cardigans, which appeared never to have been new, and heavy farm boots. She had more of the farmer in her than Jack, and gradually took over Nathan's Orchard, especially after the arrival of Perce. Between Madge and Perce there was an immediate understanding. Perce never wasted words, changed his opinions, overslept, lost his temper, raised his voice or gave way to despair. So Uncle Jack's maps and schemes were put away and he took up the study of the strategy of the Peninsula War and the Ashanti campaigns, and the composition of sentences known as "Bullets" in the weekly magazine *John Bull*.

Kate was born, our grandfather died, Rufus and Lilli returned to the still unfinished Boscombe to restore life to its hollow rooms; Joanna was born, Nathan's Orchard acquired electricity, a pipe drainage scheme and a new roof on one of the barns. The jewels, the Jews and Wormwood Scrubs were forgotten by everyone but Madge, who kept her cross handy and ready to be shouldered when anything showed signs of going well, or when Gertrude fell under the spell of a particularly attractive young man in a fashionable regiment, or when Uncle Jack won a prize for one of his "Bullets", or an invitation arrived to a wedding. The badge of shame was a great demolisher of aerial castles— a sort of snuffer to extinguish little flames of *hubris*, should they be kindled in the bosoms of any of the family. Only Perce was allowed to get away with optimistic statements, which in any case he seldom expressed.

As time went by, Aunt Madge grew more to rely on Perce's

judgement and on his company. They would spend hours together ruminating on the fecundity of cows, the performance of bulls, the price of linseed cake and the quantity of basic slag needed for Barley Ground or Cuckoo's Lea, and going through accounts kept in tattered exercise books. That the farm never paid was axiomatic; the question was how big a loss the bank would countenance and how much, on account, would quieten various creditors. This was a game as subtle as chess, but with an element of poker. One of the strengths of my aunt's position was that Uncle Jack had already been twice, or it may have been three times, declared bankrupt, so creditors had nothing to gain by invoking this process yet again. Another was that the land-lord was Rufus, who seldom, if ever, received his rent. Both Jack and Madge intended to live within their means and pay their debts. No one could have called them extravagant, unless the well-being of the dogs was at stake. It was just that making things pay was not a skill either of them possessed.

Gertrude remained at Nathan's Orchard only long enough to wash her underclothes, get her hair cut in Otterbourne, press her clothes and repack; then she was off to a house-party in Dorset, having borrowed ten shillings from Perce towards the fare. Joanna had returned to Aunt Kitty. Life seemed flat at Nathan's Orchard; I did not mind, I had plenty of books to read, but Kate got restless. It was a dead time of year. A few days later she asked her mother:

"May I go and stay with Sister Agnes?"

"Has she asked you to stay?"

"Of course. I had a letter this morning."

"I didn't see one in the post."

"I didn't know my letters were censored. Actually I got it from the postman at the gate."

Aunt Madge looked sceptical. "I see no reason why Sister Agnes should ask you to stay. After all it was she who gave you the sack."

Uncle Jack observed: "A penance, no doubt."

"You can show me the letter," Aunt Madge said. Kate gave an excellent rendering of an innocent of impeccable virtue, wedded to truth, unjustly accused, traduced and cut to the core.

"I'm sorry I so much as mentioned it. *Of course* I should have known you'd try to stop whatever I wanted to do. *Of course* I should have expected you to call me a liar. *Of course* I've invented it all. Sister Agnes didn't sack me, she stood up for me through thick and thin when those beastly sneaking girls planted half-crowns in my gym-shoes simply out of jealousy, and told a lot of lies about my getting out down the fire-escape. *Of course*, it doesn't matter a bit if I tell Sister Agnes I can't help her to run her bazaar for crippled children, because my mother won't allow me to. I'll write to her at once."

Aunt Madge merely sniffed, lit another cigarette and said in her cooing voice kept only for the dogs: "Poor little Bergamot, did Daffodil try to bite you then? Never mind, there's a sheep's head for dinner. Charity bazaars are in the summer, not at this time of year."

"This is a New Year's bazaar and Sister Agnes has a bad attack of rheumatism. But of course it doesn't matter a bit."

Aunt Madge was too old a hand to be caught like that. "I'll see the letter first."

"The old bitch," Kate said to me later. "I suppose you couldn't lend me a couple of quid?"

"I'm afraid I haven't got it." This was only too true.

"I'll try Perce." Perce, however, while willing to lend small sums to Gertrude, which eventually he got back, drew the line at Kate.

"Could you disguise your handwriting so the old girl wouldn't know it?"

"I think she's seen through the whole idea."

"You're probably right."

If one path ended in a blank wall, Kate could always find another; sooner or later, with many twists and turns, one path or the other would get her where she wanted to go. And she could coax honey from a church steeple. She harnessed Buttercup and took the pony-cart into Otterbourne. "Any luck?" I asked when she returned. Kate smiled. "There are snowdrops out on the bank below the Lydden. Do you remember the nuthatch nest we found there?" Kate was always secretive. I supposed that she would have to unfold her plan to someone because of getting to the station; she could hardly just abandon Buttercup there with the trap.

I was wrong, and she was lucky, because a cow calved in the early morning. Aunt Madge always woke early to let out the dogs, and brew herself a cup of tea on a paraffin burner; its smell permeated the whole floor, and sometimes it exploded. Next morning I heard her stumping along the landing, grumping at the dogs, the dogs pattering and scratching, soon after six o'clock. Lanterns were moving about in the blackness of the yard. Some time later I heard a car arrive and wondered if it might be the vet. Then Kate was in my room holding a candle; she wore a cloche hat and Lilli's fur jacket.

"Tell her I'll let her know when I'm coming back," she said, not bothering to whisper.

"How are you getting to the station?"

"Herbert Hiscock's taking me."

"How about cash? I think I can scrape up ten shillings . . ."

Kate laughed. "Sweet of you, coz, but I'll manage. Once in London I'll be all right. See you one of these days."

She was gone. Was she going to friends, or to _a_ friend, a cheap hotel, a Chelsea studio? You never knew with Kate. She was quite capable of ending up in a suite at the Ritz, or in a Salvation Army hostel. I dreaded a ferocious outburst from my aunt, but I need not have worried. The cow had been successfully delivered of a little heifer, and this had put Aunt Madge into an excellent humour. I found her in the kitchen having a cup of tea with Perce. Wood crackled in the newly lighted range, Nellie had gone out to the dairy to collect a jug of fresh milk and a handful of eggs, Perce had rinsed his arms and face at the sink and sat at the bare scrubbed table with his skin still glistening from the water, his hair ruffled; he had taken off his boots and was blowing on his tea, they had just shared a joke and were still smiling. There was a smell of flour and cloves and onions, of scrubbing-soap and wood smoke.

In Perce's company my aunt nearly always seemed more amiable than usual and they laughed a good deal. They shared many memories of crises overcome and tragedies submitted to, of cattle sales and horse deals, foot-and-mouth scares and milk fever; of flood and draught, bumper crops and broken binders; and endlessly they hatched plans for the future. Now they were thinking of a name for the calf and chuckling over something the carter had said. They had spun a little cocoon of their own, warm and companionable, and felt at home in it together. Perce did not mind how much the dogs scratched and made messes, and Aunt Madge admired Perce's strength and competence and uneroded self-esteem. There was a simplicity in their relationship. I felt sorry for Uncle Jack.

"Kate told me to tell you she's gone to the station and that she'll let you know when she's coming back." Aunt Madge merely looked surprised.

"Buttercup's in the stable. Kate hasn't *walked?*"

"No, Herbert Hiscock took her."

"Good heavens, she hasn't taken up with *him*, has she?"

"He's bespoke," Perce said. "If Jim Pickering will let Miss Grace have 'im."

"Old Pickering's too proud," Aunt Madge remarked. "My father spoilt him."

"They was good friends."

"Pickering's a clever man. But that doesn't mean no one's good enough for his daughters."

They seemed more inclined to gossip about the Pickering family than to take note of Kate's departure. You never knew with Aunt Madge, who did not even inquire her daughter's destination.

"Kate's gone to London, I think," I volunteered.

"London! A lot of good that'll do her, silly little fool. She's got no money. What she needs is a proper coat and skirt, instead of spending what she *has* got on gadding about."

"They'm all the same when they'm young. Same as a filly'll kick up his heels soon as he's in the paddock."

"We haven't had a Fillpail for some time," my aunt recalled, going back to the calf. "That was a good family."

"Y'm. There was Parsley. Carries his blood."

"I wouldn't mind a Fillpail again."

"Very good, m'm." Perce never argued, and now and again, just to observe the proprieties, put in a servant-to-employer word or phrase. I was not surprised, a week or two later, to find the calf referred to as Parsley. As it was a heifer, it was known as "he". All the men on the farm called cows, hens, mares and sows "he" and the males of the species "she", which made things most confusing. I never did discover why.

8

It was quiet at Nathan's Orchard without Kate or Gert. There was the daily walking of the dogs on Kingscliffe and over sodden fields; snowdrops coming out in the orchard; Otterbourne in the pony-trap to fetch veterinary medicines; the smell of boiling tripe; Perce with his ruddy face and slow, half-humorous manner drying his stockinged feet before the kitchen range; collecting eggs from straw in the barn, from a disused manger, from behind a harrow lying half in and half out of a shed; helping Nellie to skim the big milk-pans and turn the creaking churn and squeeze out the buttermilk, and pat up the sweet-smelling fresh butter with Scotch hands and make criss-cross patterns on the surface, and then stamp them with a round wooden die that left an imprint of a swan, a thistle or a sailing ship. And there were plenty of books to read.

All the same, I had begun to look forward to returning to Reading, and the hurrying from lecture to lecture, and coffees in the Buttery, and teas at the Central Café in the town, and the smell of formalin in labs, and the sound of the trams; even cold winds whining down the tow-path and along Redlands Road. And of course Turner, who was spending his vacation playing rugger, beagling and visiting his favourite pubs. I had received a Christmas card from him, and a postcard with a picture of a comic cow making a lewd remark about a bull.

So I was glad when the day came for Uncle Jack to drive me to the station. We had little to say to each other. My interest in the Peninsula War and the Ashanti campaigns was minimal; for his part, Reading was a railway junction in a dirty town where biscuits were made. On the local platform Uncle Jack waited in a silence painful to us both until the train came in, gave me two half-crowns and said: "I hope you'll find a seat."

"I expect I shall."

"Be careful if you lean out of the window. Last time I travelled on this line I got a nasty smut in the eye."

"They can be awfully painful."

"My eye was inflamed for several days."

"Well, goodbye, Uncle Jack, and thank you for having me."

"I expect your aunt has warned you not to speak to strange men. All girls are told that, I believe. I don't remember boys being told not to speak to strange women, but should think that

warning even more desirable." He gave a snort, and the smile
that suddenly revealed traces of his old charm and gaiety.

"Not that advice from elders has the least importance. Anyway, in nine cases out of ten it's wrong. The only advice my
father gave me that was any use was on my twenty-first birthday. He said: 'Never ask a man how he voted or what he paid
for a horse.' I never have."

"Thank you, Uncle Jack, I'll remember that," I promised.

Chapter Ten

THE Hilary term at Reading—we followed Oxford in our terminology—was so unpleasant out of doors that, for the most part, people stayed in, and sometimes worked; but no one admitted to this. A curious attitude prevailed towards study, which I suppose also derived from Oxford tradition. It was regarded as a secret, almost shameful practice, like masturbation or sucking sweets; no doubt people indulged in it from time to time but they kept quiet about it, and pretended that nothing was further from their thoughts.

If an undergraduate was caught out entering the library on a fine afternoon, he made some excuse about having nowhere to sit in his digs to write a letter. Studying had mainly to be done late at night when no one was likely to catch you at it. It would have been dreadfully *infra dig* to have openly admitted to a regular routine of study, or to any other attitude towards it but that of dislike and contempt. This did not apply to Edu's, who were known to work quite openly—no doubt a reason for their pariahdom; and certain exceptions were made. About a fortnight, or possibly three weeks, before examinations, it suddenly became respectable to sit up all night mugging things up: in itself, a proof that nothing had been mugged for the first eight weeks or so of term.

While we did our best to pursue, at a considerable distance, the Oxford tradition, we could not follow it all the way, for example to the extent of never going to lectures. In our case lectures were more or less compulsory, and so were "practicals" in the laboratories. Our Dean, a small, squat, ugly, rather savage Midlander who taught biochemistry, spitting out the formulae as if they had been so many oaths, kept us under a discipline closer to that of school than university. I do not recall that anyone defied this. Dutifully, we carried our notebooks about and recorded the gist of our lectures; this amounted almost to dictation in some cases.

Sidney Pennington, our Professor of Agriculture, made no

bones about it and dispensed his wisdom at dictation speed, as if
we had been children learning French; we could scarcely have
departed farther from the tutorial system. It was in the labs
more than in the lecture rooms that we acquired a smattering of
the biological sciences. And very much a smattering it was,
because our field was so wide. On the one hand were the basic
sciences: chemistry, divided firmly down the middle into organic
and inorganic, flanked on one side by physics and geology, and
on the other by botany, zoology, entomology and bacteriology;
on the other hand were non-scientific subjects such as agricultural history and economics, with a glance at accountancy, farm
management and law. On top of all that we spent many wet,
cold and inconclusive afternoons trudging round the university
farm learning how to mark out a field for ploughing, to distinguish Yorkshire fog from cocksfoot and sainfoin from broad red
clover, to master the show points of bulls, cows, pigs and fat
bullocks, and to calculate the areas of fields.

Nevertheless it was a course that opened many windows, at
least for me, to whom the whole field of natural sciences had
hitherto lain in total darkness. So the simplest of facts, like the
composition of a cell or the structure of a stamen, came with all
the force of revelation; the things that went on under your nose,
yet totally without your knowledge, were unbelievable. Even
the table you were sitting at, the handkerchief with which you
blew your nose, was fantastically intricate; a controlled, law-
abiding universe of whirling atoms, each with a nucleus of
orbiting particles like a universe in miniature, held together
by a balance of electrical charges; and as for what came out of
your nose into the handkerchief, billion upon billion of living
creatures, each reproducing, eating, breathing and moving—
this simply could not be taken in. Yet it was true. I remember
being more or less bowled over by the complex life history of
the liver fluke, and the nature of viruses that straddle the border
between life and non-life, and by the realization that there
really is no hard and fast line between the two. The microscope
opened up a whole new world of drama and mystery, and of
beauty too; the shapes and patterns of wriggling bacteria, of
purple-stained cells splitting and re-forming, of the thread-like
mycelia of fungi and their intricate spores, contained for me all

the wonder that students of art experience when they first set eyes on the great artistic masterpieces of the world. It was tantalizing to know how little we could learn of these things, like water-beetles tacking about on the surface of knowledge, conscious that beneath us lay depths we should never fathom, and at whose secrets we could only guess.

In our leisure hours, the cinema was almost our only interest apart from sport and, of course, ourselves; our only artistic interest one would say, if this did not pitch the tone a good deal too high. One cinema catered to what might, by stretching a point, have been described as more highbrow tastes, in that its management sometimes revived an interesting old film or put on a foreign one, generally German. These UFA pictures were the intellectual fashion of the day, just as French ones became a little later, and Italian productions later still. This was the heyday of Emil Jannings, glooming through doom-laden, turgid dramas of a Germany ravaged by inflation, full of night-clubs and perverts and shady deals. These films had also Marlene Dietrich in her early splendour, to us the epitome of sophistication and glamour.

There was also Rudolf Valentino, whose vehicles, as the expression was, were gloriously fusty, over-wrought and creaking old coaches, but knew how to move an audience. *The Sheikh* —*The Four Horsemen*—*Blood and Sand*—their names still evoke the ghost of ravishment. We affected to despise Rudolf Valentino and ribald shouts, cheers, whistles and ironical clapping sometimes emerged from the one-and-fours, but we went to see his films all the same, and succombed to the vogue they introduced for the tango: a British version of the tango, that is, a good deal removed from the Latin. No dance became complete without several tangos, executed with a snake-like glide and in a series of little rushes, clasping your partner's hand high above your head; at the end of each rush you pivoted and glided back again; the music was stirring, the exercise strenuous and it all seemed exotic, adventurous and new.

It was, however, easy to make a hash of the tango, and I formed an ambition to learn it properly. A dancing school in Reading advertised a special course in six lessons for ten-and-sixpence, conducted by Señor Ramon Hidalgo of Buenos Aires.

Ten-and-six was more than I could afford; but I had set my heart on these lessons and puzzled over how to raise it. I sadly missed the satisfying postal orders for ten shillings that formerly had come my way, from time to time, from the *East African Standard* for reports of local polo matches; so far as I knew there was no polo in Reading, and, if there had been, the *Reading Mercury* was unlikely to be interested in my contributions.

I had tried already several other avenues without success. Inspired by Uncle Jack, I had experimented fruitlessly with Bullets and with other competitions, and received rejection slips from several sources for short stories and informative little pieces on colonial policy in Africa, A Day in the Life of a Coffee Planter, the History of the Durham Ox and From a View to a Kill with the Blankshire. Such English relatives as I knew of, apart from those at Nathan's Orchard, were elusive, broke or total strangers. I had nothing I could sell except my portable gramophone, which I could not bear to part with, and a few necessary text books. Part-time jobs were not available in those days.

I had more or less abandoned hope when I got a letter from an uncle who, like most of my relations, I had either never seen, or not encountered since infancy. He was my father's half-brother, much younger, and something of a mythical character; the sort of man who was heard of either hiring a private railway coach to convey a splendid party to the Grand National, or else down and out in Dieppe, or possibly exchanging a consignment of muzzle-loaders for Maria Teresa dollars in Addis Ababa. I expect these exploits were exaggerated, and actually he worked for a firm in the City connected with something like jute. His letter invited me to lunch at the Carlton grill. If he was prepared to spend at least a pound, I argued, on giving me a meal, he might consider spending it instead on improving my education, or at any rate my social poise.

Instead of luncheon, I suggested, I would appreciate an opportunity to take a special course outside the normal curriculum, that I could not otherwise afford. By return I got an envelope without a letter, but with a five-pound note. I had never seen one before and could hardly believe it. But a bank changed it, and I wrote so fervently to Uncle Alex that I afterwards feared he would think I was buttering him up in the hopes of getting more.

The tango lessons were held in a chilly, dimly illuminated room above a café, with yellowish-brown walls and a splintery floor revealed by rolling back a worn turkey carpet. A lady with one of those black spangled shawls you used to get at Simon Artz in Port Said draped around her skinny shoulders sat at an upright piano, in need of tuning, thumping out Latin airs. Señor Ramon Hidalgo was suitably swarthy, polite (one might have said smarmy) and proficient at his art, though it was a pity he was tubby and heavy-hipped; he did not look at all like Rudolf Valentino. Tufts of hair grew out of his ears, and his breath was flavoured sometimes by brandy and sometimes by onion.

I had kept my intentions dark, and had not expected to encounter any colleagues; I was in for several surprises. The first of these was the hefty and familiar form of Dando. She overtopped the Señor by several inches, and stood four-square among the narrow-chested typists and anaemic shop-assistants who formed the bulk of his pupils like a sturdy forest tree among second-growth saplings. From a creased brown velveteen dress protruded brawny forearms toughened by frequent immersion in ice-encrusted water troughs and by rolling milk-churns across muddy yards. She wore her hair in plaits wound tightly about her head to form a sort of helmet, and her weather-beaten face, with small and deep-set eyes, had, beneath its stolidity, the wary, uncertain look of a nervous pony. She must have taken size eight in shoes. Could Thomas be the reason for her enrolment under Señor Hidalgo? It seemed unlikely. She was evidently as embarrassed at encountering me, as I was startled by her presence; tongue-tied at the best of times, she acted as if she had been caught out in some highly discreditable act and almost literally hung her head in shame.

"I didn't expect to find you here."

"Limbers one up," she muttered.

"I wish it was warmer in here."

She looked astonished. "*Warmer*? It's awfully hot."

"Perhaps you've got a thick vest."

"Of course."

Further remarks were drowned by the thumping of the piano. Señor Hidalgo gave a demonstration with one of his star pupils, veering over backwards at a dangerous angle and pointing up-stretched arms like masts towards the ceiling; then, each swinging out a leg, they pivoted and got into reverse, dashing swiftly across the room in a sort of pounce. "Ips steady! Ips steady!" cried the Señor. "Ze knees bent! Now we all try! Partners, please."

I moved hastily away from Dando; I had nothing against her as a person but as a partner she would be terrifying. Girls out-numbered men by three or four to one. I felt my shoulder tapped, turned round and there—he must have just arrived—was Turner. Dando's tongue could not have been more tied than mine.

"Dr. Livingstone," Turner said, without originality but with one eyebrow raised. "How steady are your ips? Shall we try?"

With his athlete's nimble-footedness, Turner was a natural dancer and it was delightful to be partnered by him even when neither of us knew the steps; Señor Hidalgo's rendering of them was a simple one, and quite soon we found ourselves skating about the splintery floor with bent knees and outstretched arms, pivoting and swaying on one leg and making little rushes in a very spirited fashion. All we needed was a fringed shawl and castanets for me and a sombrero with a chin-strap, black tights and a white silk shirt open to the waist for Turner. Instead he wore a polo-necked sweater.

"Hot work, this," he said. "Worse than rugger."

"Ips steady! Ips steady!" the Señor exhorted. "The knee stiff, the right leg swing round behind the left foot, so! The body supple, shoulders free, let go, let go! Remember the pampas, the estanchio, the hot blood of the south!" His pudgy face glistened, and our palms and armpits were moist. "For God's sake pump a bit more guts into it, Ivy," I heard him admonish the pianist as we swept by. "The rhythm of the pampas!" he called to his pupils. "Elbows straight! Ips steady! Knees bent!" Dando thundered past, her face creased into a frown of concentration, attached to a girl half her size, with rabbit teeth, jade-green ear-rings frenziedly swaying, and knock-knees.

Our half hour's instruction went all too soon. It was still early. "Can I see you home?" Turner offered. "With the rhythm of the pampas in your blood, Señor Hidalgo will have you signed up for Buenos Aires before you can unsteady your ips. D'you think that's the idea behind it all? A recruiting drive?"

Our fellow-pupils were swathing themselves in mufflers, macintoshes and galoshes in the hallway, visions of pampas and estanchio quickly fading into the prospect of dark back-streets of Reading wet with drizzle, a cold east wind, a smell of grime and smoke and fish-and-chips, the clattering and puffing of locomotives in a nearby shunting yard, and a trudge back to cold bed-sitters in cheap lodging houses, each one tightly sealed behind its little strip of privet hedge. Our lessons took place in one of the seedier, less reputable sections of the city, which I had been told was the second most immoral in England; the first was Nottingham. How, I inquired, did you measure the immorality of a city? Perhaps by the statistics of venereal disease. And why should people be more immoral if they lived in Nottingham or Reading, than, say, in Leicester or Leeds? No one knew.

"It mightn't need a lot of persuasion," I remarked, thinking of signing up as a white slave.

"They drug you first, I believe."

"Even without being drugged."

Every time the door opened to emit a home-goer, a bitter blast swept into the hallway. Dando's rabbit-toothed partner, bundled into waterproofs and woollens, plunged out with a wave and bright: "Well, ta-ta, dear. So long, all." Dando herself pulled on galoshes, oilskins and woollen gloves and stood like a willing but uneasy horse, only too clearly waiting for me to suggest that we walk back together. Feeling horribly mean, I muttered something about seeing her later and ducked through the door.

On the way home we stopped at a pub for half a pint in the saloon bar. This was a very dashing thing to do; against the rules, in fact; women undergraduates were not allowed to enter pubs; if caught, they might get sent down. The danger was minimal, however: there were no proctors and Swift, for instance, often frequented pubs, or so she told us, and had never

been so much as cautioned; still, you never knew, so pubs had
an aura of wickedness about them which little to be seen in the
Three Cups appeared to justify. The air was thick with tobacco
smoke, the tables sloppy with spilled beer, the triangular ash-
trays overflowing. Turner played darts with practised skill and
no one molested me as I sat alone at my small table with my
half pint—I never liked beer—trying to feel that I was seeing
life, even if not in Buenos Aires.

The customers looked drab, pallid and grubby; they really
did wear mufflers and cloth caps in those days, and no ties, and
spat sometimes into corners, and had bad teeth to a man. But
they were very respectable; also poor, and could seldom afford
more than a pint, even at sixpence a time, so drunkenness was
rare, though now and again someone was lucky with the horses.
The working classes inhabited a different world entirely from
our own; a mysterious, slightly menacing and hostile world
that most of us had little inclination to explore because, no
doubt, of suppressed guilt; there but for the grace of God went
all of us, and there we might one day find ourselves if we were
failures. We believed it to be a world that was nasty, brutish
and cruel, although such individuals we personally encountered
were almost always friendly, cheerful and polite. This dis-
crepancy we never tried to reconcile, and such notions applied
only to industrial workers in cities—country folk were different
and lived in the same kind of way as we did, only on even less
money, and had more or less the same ideas.

When Turner came back, I felt an unexpected spasm of
despair. "I don't suppose it's any good learning the tango."

"Why not? Good, healthy exercise."

"I'll never get a chance to do it."

"You might find yourself out on the pampas any day."

"Is Snugg good at it?"

"Maisie? Born with the click of castanets in her ears. They're
famous for their tangos in Edgbaston."

"Where's that?"

"Part of Birmingham." There it came again—I never knew
where anything was, or what went on there. "They always have
a tango on the green at Edgbaston on Rogation Sunday, dressed
as bullfighters and bullfighters' molls. The Bishop blesses them,

the Warden of the Cinque Ports tosses a tortilla and the first girl to grab a mouthful will have blue-eyed twins next Oak Apple Day, one of whom will marry a king's daughter. It's something to do with the defeat of the Armada. You ought to see it one day."

For all I knew, this might be true. English tribal customs were just as odd as those of Africans. I wanted to know how serious his attachment was to Snugg, or whether he just found her convenient. All I could say was:

"I've never been to Birmingham."

"I played rugger there once. They call the middle part the Bull Ring. Hence the Edgebaston tango, I expect."

"I didn't know there was ever bullfighting in England."

"We'd better move on, or your friend Dando will be sending out a search-party with her pack of mastiffs. She does keep mastiffs, doesn't she?"

"Bloodhounds, actually."

"Much the same, I daresay."

It was drizzling steadily all the way home. Reading kept its immorality very dark. The streets through which we trudged towards the London Road were almost deserted. No sound of revelry emerged from pubs or fish-and-chip shops; all we could hear was a distant rattle of trams and the chuff and thud of shunting locomotives. Even games of pavement hopscotch had been quenched. Many waters cannot quench love, neither can the floods devour it . . . They seemed to have quenched it in Reading.

"Feels like snow," Turner remarked.

"Isn't it too late in the year?"

"It's never too late for snow."

Even though the curtains were drawn and the crescent deserted, a wary presence seemed to invest my lodging-house, an unformulated warning. Perhaps it was Snugg's aura—she believed in auras, so she said; they changed colour.

"Will you come in?"

"I'd better not, thanks all the same."

We stood in the doorway uncertainly and torn, in my case, between the impulse to nestle, and the awful fear of scaring him away; young men, despite their wolf-like intentions, were well known to be as easily frightened off as mice that, smelling human scent upon the trap, resist the lure of cheese. A designing female was a female shunned. Still, he had laid himself out to please, and surely no chinks showed through the drawn curtains? I moved hesitantly a half-step closer; everything smelt of wet Burberry. One eyebrow went up and there was a nice warm kiss that made me tingle all over, but all too quickly ended; a brief hug and he was gone.

Chapter Eleven

THE fire in the sitting room was out; it generally died by nine o'clock for lack of fuel. Dando looked up from a treatise on the ripening of cheese and said sepulchrally: "You were wanted on the telephone."

This had never happened before. "Who by?"

"A man." She made this seem extremely sinister. "He sounded faint," she added.

The telephone was pretty silent as a rule. Students seldom called each other, if only because it cost twopence; either you ran into people in the cloisters or Buttery, or left a note at their digs. A call might mean bad news from home—generally speaking, only bad news justified the expense of a trunk call; good news could be written. There were exceptions; Dando had received a call when one of the bloodhounds had carried off an open championship at Exeter, and Swift was liable to be summoned to the instrument, which was in the hall and anything but private, by Abdul, who had a most reckless attitude towards twopences. The conversations seemed to consist of monologues by Abdul, who was evidently subject to fits of depression and in need of cheering up; now and again heartening phrases such as: "Well, keep your pecker up, old boy," or: "Never say die, it's a great life if you don't weaken," could be heard in Swift's cheery tones as one of us passed through the hall, letting in a blast of cold air from the street.

The mystery was solved the following evening when an all but inaudible voice claimed to be that of Jumbo Matheson and invited me to the promised *thé dansant*. This called for a visit to the Guinea Shop, thanks to the residue of Uncle Alex's fiver. I boldly plunged for something scarlet, adorned with little silver bells, which I hoped would be suitable; I had no idea what was worn at *thé dansants*. I could not resist informing Snugg, in a casual manner, that I was going to London on Saturday by car.

"Lucky you," said Snugg. "A show, I suppose?"

"I daresay. Or we might go to a *thé dansant*."

126

"That'll give you a chance to show off your tango." Her tone was waspish.

How had she found out? Had Turner told her—or Dando, turned into a snake in the grass? There was little you could do at Reading without being found out.

Unless it was actually pelting, the hood of Jumbo's jalopy was kept down, and putting it up—a major operation—made scarcely any difference. I was anxious about the scarlet frock, which did not look as if it would stand up to a good soaking, and thankful when Saturday turned out to be one of those cold and blustery but fine, crisp spring days, with scudding clouds and patches of blue sky. Although the trees were black as charcoal, and splendid in their winter tracery, the elms looked as if they had been dusted with a dark red powder and the whippy willows had a purplish tinge.

Even Jumbo looked somehow brighter and larger than I remembered him: still pop-eyed, with a little blunt nose and too small a mouth, but neat and tidy in a well-pressed dark grey suit. It was a great pity that English custom forbade officers to wear uniform when off duty; Jumbo would have looked twice the man in Naval attire. Abroad, I understood, officers went about covered with gold braid and epaulettes and clanking with spurs and swords, which I thought preferable, but my father had been very scornful about all the ironmongery, as he said, worn by foreigners, including students, in his youth, in Germany. Once, when visiting Heidelberg, he had tripped over someone's sword in a beer-garden, and a young man with scars down both cheekbones had challenged him to a duel. After an orgy of heel-clicking, saluting and talk of seconds and weapons and doctors, my father had packed his bag and left in the night, ignoble but unscarred. It was hard to imagine Turner, for instance, or Thomas, or even Viney, going about in swords. These weapons would have been distracting in lectures and awkward in the Buttery.

"This is much more fun than watching hockey or going to the flicks."

"Well, I *hope* it will be. She was missing a bit coming along and the clutch is slipping rather."

"Isn't there rather an odd noise?"

"A bit of a knock. I hope it's not the big end." It began to look as if a long hike rather than a tango was to be our portion, and I had the wrong shoes.

"I've never been to a *thé dansant* before." One thing about Jumbo, you didn't mind admitting ignorance; he would never make you feel small.

"As a matter of fact, nor have I."

"Oh. What does one do?"

"I don't think one *does* anything exactly. It's more a question of the time of day."

"You mean they're *thé dansants* in the afternoon and just dances in the evening?"

"Yes. Because of the *thé*."

The jalopy had a bout of feverish coughing and Jumbo looked anxious; however, it seemed to clear itself of some obstruction and bowled along through Maidenhead, across the glittering river and on to Slough, already pretty hideous and sprawling but nothing like as awful as it was destined to become.

"As a matter of fact," Jumbo said, "this is a bit of a celebration."

"Your birthday?"

"A spot of promotion."

"Oh, well done." This would make him into a second lieutenant and remove him from the *Periwinkle*—all the way, he said, to Hong Kong. Unexpectedly, I felt a pang of loss. Jumbo was not exciting but he grew on you, and it was reassuring to feel that he was there.

"What will you do with Patch?" Patch was the cocker spaniel.

"That's the snag. I can't very well leave him at home because there's no one to exercise him; my mother's pretty bad with rheumatism these days. He gets so fat without exercise."

"I'm afraid I can't suggest Nathan's Orchard. It's rather over-populated already, from a canine point of view."

"You don't suppose that bloodhound woman of yours might take him?"

"My bloodhound woman? Oh, you mean Dando."

"Yes. She says they're awfully good-natured. Of course I'd pay for his keep."

"Well, we could ask."

For once, Jumbo had not mentioned Gertrude. I hoped he was at last succeeding in stamping out his unrequited love.

The Criterion, to which we duly came, turned out to be a place of great sophistication, glamour and romance. The lights were dim, small tables surrounded a crowded dance floor as smooth as satin; waiters in tails came and went as deftly as swallows; the men were in dark lounge suits, the women in short, straight, shiny frocks, cloche hats and high heels, with shingled hair; seductive music beat and murmured like the throbbing of a powerful heart, with a jungly undertone. The singer was a Negro of international fame, and I had some of his records. To see him in the flesh was wonderful beyond my dreams. He was an attractive coffee-colour, with a small moustache, very white teeth and sad, weary eyes.

This was a *thé dansant* in style. And all, so far as I remember, for half-a-crown, which included as many thin cress sandwiches and iced cakes as you wanted, and pots of China tea. Here indeed was Life, and I was grateful to Jumbo for taking me to see it. We secured a little table some way back from the dance floor, which was packed; you could not do much actual dancing, but felt that at any minute you might bump into someone like Ivor Novello or Tallulah Bankhead. Saxophones wailed, moaned and beckoned you down paths of mystery and allurement, permeating your blood like sugar. This was the age of crooners, and there was Berry, crooning away.

> "Me and the boy friend, the boy friend and me,
>   We love each other, as Russians love tea . . ."

"Do Russians really love tea do you suppose? I thought it was vodka."

"I doubt if they get either now, they're starving. I believe they've eaten all the dogs and cats."

"How awful!"

"Lovely dogs, too, like those Borzois. And big white ones called Samoyids I think, or something like it."

"Perhaps you'll get a Pekinese in China."

"I should be afraid of their eyes dropping out. I'd rather have a Chow."

"Yes, a Chow would be nice."

9

The band had moved on to a more vigorous rhythm and the saxophonists were writhing like snakes.

"... the meanest girl in town:
Now making love to Hannah in a big arm-chair
Is like strolling through Alaska in your underwear ..."

We were reprieved from a chat about Alaska, leading on no doubt to Huskies, by an unexpected hail from a nearby table; and there, dimly discerned through the half-lit haze, clad in a very short, straight smock patterned with enormous yellow flowers, was my cousin Kate. She waved energetically. Her companion was a grizzly-bearded individual with a lean and hungry look and a corduroy jacket, out of place among the dark lounge suits; he had a floppy tie and could only be a painter. I waved back.

"Fancy running into Kate."

This had a bad effect on Jumbo. "You don't suppose that Gertrude ..."

"No, I don't. It's the point-to-point season. Gert's probably freezing to death in a field somewhere, wrapped in rugs and eating cold chicken and drinking port from a flask."

Kate came over to our table walking in the sort of slouching way that was fashionable; hers was the flat contemporary figure that had eliminated breasts, and she had long ear-rings, and a cigarette holder, and a lot of beads. It was hard to recall that we had once climbed apple trees together, and slid off hayricks, and opened a gate for motorists on the common to collect pennies which we spent at Mr. Hodge the grocer's on bullseyes and acid drops.

"Come and meet Berry," she said offhandedly.

"You mean you *know* him?"

She gave a tinkling sort of laugh. "Of course I know Berry. Everyone knows him."

"Yes, but everyone ..." Everyone was the world of stage celebrities and society hostesses who appeared week after week in the *Tatler*; Berry had been "taken up" by them, and I could hardly believe that Kate had wriggled into those circles, even from her vantage point near Bushey Park. All the same, it turned out to be true that she knew Berry, because he came over to their table during a break and sat down and smiled at her, crinkling his eyes in a breath-taking manner. Kate said: "Meet my cousin, Berry," and he said "Hiya, baby," and started a conversation with the painter, if painter he was, about lousy scabs and cuts and bucks and rackets and joints and squeezes; it was beyond my range, but I disentangled cash as its theme. Jumbo just sat and goggled. A waiter brought a pot of tea.

"I wouldn't have expected Berry to drink tea," I suggested.

"Spiked, I guess." Kate was going American.

"Who's your friend with the beard?"

"Do you mean to say you don't know Shamus?"

"Why should I know him?"

"He's just about the most famous painter in London, if not in the world. You must have seen the row about his portrait of Tallulah Bankhead as the Virgin Mary, with Gertrude Stein as Joseph?"

"I don't know that I did."

"Now he's doing Berry. He says Berry has the shapeliest buttocks he's ever seen. That's one of Shamus's words, shapeliest. He says he's going to paint Berry as Abraham Lincoln at the battle of Gettysburg. It'll be a sensation."

"I should think it would. Did you meet him at Miss Hapgold's?"

"Well, round and about . . ."

Kate evidently got round and about a lot. "He wants to come down and paint daddy," she added. "He saw a snapshot, and said daddy has a head like the Egyptian Pharaohs, and that it comes about by in-breeding, brothers and sisters for centuries."

"I should hardly think that Uncle Jack . . ."

"Shamus will have to pretend he wants to paint the dogs. He's quite used to farms and muddle. He was brought up in an Irish bog with no shoes living on potatoes and shared a manger with a cow called Persephone. The only thing is, he might want to bring Berry. While he's painting the portrait, he says, Berry is like an embryo joined to him by an umbilical cord."

"You know, Kate, that Shamus—is it?—he's old enough to be your father."

"Yes. In fact, he thinks he may *be* my father."

"It seems unlikely that Aunt Madge visited the bog and shared a manger with him and the cow Persephone."

"He'd left the bog by then and was in Paris, eking out a living as a waiter. One day a beautiful English girl came to his café with her father, an important man with a bushy black beard. She had golden hair and a sad expression and a miniature poodle and the chestnuts were in flower and they had an affair, or at any rate they slept together once and it was in the right year."

"Surely Aunt Madge never went to Paris, let alone picked up a waiter in a café."

"She might have. After daddy got put inside, I believe grandpa took her abroad to cure his gout and drown her sorrows. They could easily have stayed in Paris on the way. And Shamus said that the bearded man had a watch-chain with a little gold key."

Kate's tales were always so plausible, you found yourself believing them against your will. Shamus was declaiming in a high-pitched voice to Berry; he had a long, narrow face and a glittering eye like the Ancient Mariner's, and a long nose. I glanced at Kate; she had a narrow face and a longish nose; so had Uncle Jack and so, apparently, had the ancient Pharaohs. "Aunt Madge never had a poodle." I objected.

"She might have had. Shamus would account for my talent, of course."

It would account for much. "You see that couple over there, the girl in a green frock?" The dancers were Black Bottoming, flinging their buttocks from side to side and kicking up their heels like frisky horses to the rhythm welling, as it seemed, from the very bowels of an agonized saxophonist. "She's actually a man. The green frock one, I mean."

Poor Jumbo, who had been gazing at Kate with his mouth half open and his eyes more like gooseberries than ever, made an inarticulate sound.

"Quite a lot of girls are really men. This is one of the places where they come." With the Eton crops and flat figures then in fashion, it was indeed hard to tell which was which, apart from dress. "Their legs are straighter as a rule and their feet are larger than a real girl's," Kate explained. "Though not always. That's one thing about Shamus, you know where you are."

Berry took his leave with a wave, a crinkly smile, and a "Bye, baby." Only four words of his had come my way, in two helpings, but I treasured them; at least they had been addressed directly at me. Jumbo, visibly shaken, led me back to the dance floor. He was not a bad dancer as a rule, but now kept looking round him nervously and failing to concentrate. "Surely she must have made that up, about the girls being men."

"She makes up a good deal."

"I suppose it's a gift in a way, especially if she's going to be an artist. But when one thinks of Gertrude . . . You'd never believe them to be sisters, would you?"

"Half-sisters, according to Kate."

"I was going to suggest your cousin Kate might like to come down to Pompey with us and see *Periwinkle* before I leave. But I'm not really sure . . ."

"You never know with Kate. The Captain might turn out to be her half-brother."

"I hardly think so. He was centre-three-quarters for Scotland."

"Well, Aunt Madge might have stayed in Edinburgh as well as in Paris."

I had gone too far.

"I expect I'm hopelessly old-fashioned, but there are subjects I was brought up to believe one didn't joke about."

We made it up on the way home; Jumbo apologized, which in his turn was a mistake. He was born to be a doormat, poor Jumbo, and not many women really want to become boots. However, we arranged a trip to Portsmouth in the Easter vacation, and in due course Jumbo collected me from Nathan's Orchard. He was in uniform, and it was surprising what a difference this made; he looked larger, and twice as much at ease. Even the jalopy seemed less wheezy as we wound along lanes like tunnels, passing close to South Molton, where Jumbo's home lay. He was reticent about his home, I suppose because it was a humble one, without a farm, a shoot, a river or even a covert suitable for foxes; his mother lived, I gathered, on the outskirts of the town, and had nothing but a small garden, too small for exercising Patch in, even if her rheumatics had allowed her to go for walks. His father had been in the Navy before him but had not, disappointingly, been killed in action or gone down with his ship; he had been struck in Plymouth by a tram which crushed his leg, and the leg had gone septic, at the age of thirty-two.

Periwinkle was small and cramped, and there was a lot of scrambling up and down ladders and in and out of hatches; the ward-room seemed little bigger than a railway carriage, and I could see that it would be an advantage for Jumbo to be small. The commanding officer, however, was not small at all but broad and brawny and looked much more as a Naval officer should, wearing his cap at a dashing angle like Admiral Beattie and speaking in a deep, gruff voice. Everyone was welcoming and friendly, and merely to be in a ship that flew the White Ensign was a thrill greater even than that of meeting Berry. It was wonderful to see how white and scoured the decks were, how every rope was neatly coiled, and to learn that the casks in which the rum ration reached the fleet bore on their bottoms a red hieroglyphic copied from Nelson's own hand, or so I was told. And of course there was the smell of the sea, and tar and ropes, and salt and bilge, and seaweed and the things that are unloaded and loaded into holds, so although there was not much to see in *Periwinkle*, I enjoyed my day. We had tea at the largest hotel to the music of an orchestra playing from behind potted palms, and I asked Jumbo if he had decided what to do about Patch when he went to China.

"There's nothing settled yet," he said.

"If you like I can ask Aunt Madge."

"That's awfully kind, but I think he'd be swamped if you know what I mean. As a matter of fact . . ."

I passed him a cake and made an encouraging sound.

"I hope she didn't think it awful cheek, but actually I wrote to your friend at Reading."

"You mean Dando?"

"Yes. I suppose it *was* cheek but she seemed to take an interest in Patch, and I thought she might know of someone who sort of took in boarders, if you know what I mean."

"And did she?"

"She sent a very encouraging reply."

I did not like to press Jumbo any further, but felt that something more was afoot. Perhaps she was going to take Patch herself, among the bloodhounds; at any rate I should hear about it at the start of the summer term. Strengthened, however, by cups of tea and slices of chocolate cake, Jumbo summoned up courage to add: "Actually she may be coming to stay."

"You mean with your mother?"

"Just for a day or two, to see if Patch would fit in, as it were. She said she was coming in this direction anyway for a show."

"What a jolly good plan!" I overdid the enthusiasm. "You must feel awfully relieved to know that Patch'll be provided for. I'm sure he couldn't have a better home."

"Nothing's settled yet of course. It's just an idea."

On the way home we ran into fog and crawled along the lanes, our weak headlights bouncing off an endless wall of dense cotton-wool. Navigating through fog before the invention of cat's-eyes and the covering-in of open ditches was a nerve-racking affair. We ran out of it close to Nathan's Orchard and arrived very late, in clear starlight, to find my aunt and uncle waiting up resentfully and coldly, having let out the fire.

"There are no fogs," my uncle said firmly, "at this time of year."

"But there *was* a fog, Uncle Jack."

"A fog is the result of condensation of moisture when saturated air rises to encounter a colder current from above: in other words, when the temperature is falling. At this season of the year the nights are cold and days are warmer—in other words the conditions are reversed. So fogs are impossible."

"But *this* fog——"

"Argue, argue, argue," snapped my aunt. "I don't know what your poor mother would say if she knew what was going on behind her back."

"To be out late is one thing," Uncle Jack added. "It's quite another to invent a pack of lies and excuses."

"But——" Although I knew it was stupid to argue, the injustice was hard to swallow; I had not yet learnt the painful lesson that people act not on what is so, but on what they want to think is so; and that generally they shun, rather than seek, the truth. If my uncle and aunt did not want the fog to be there, they would see stars through a pea-souper, and one should play Katherine to their Petruchio and turn the sun into the moon and back again to keep out out of trouble.

Besides, truth was seldom as simple as the matter of the fog. I had wondered several times, for instance, how much truth there was, if any, in Kate's story of her mother, Shamus and the Parisian café. Uncle Jack was fair, Kate was dark—that was nothing; both had long heads, and so had Shamus; Kate's eyes were like her mother's. After the dogs had poured out into the night barking, returned one by one and been gathered in, the door chained and bolted, ash-trays emptied into a cold grate, I asked Aunt Madge if she had ever owned a poodle.

"Certainly not."

"You've always stuck to terriers?"

"Always."

"You had a pug once," Uncle Jack reminded her.

"A pug! Never."

"Don't you remember that pug your father gave you?"

"*He* may have had a pug. I never had one."

"Really, darling, I'm surprised you've forgotten. You were very fond of it at one time. Satan—Sable—Sailor—something like that."

"You see, you can't remember its name. I can't remember any pug. My mother had one called Archibald."

"This was not Archibald. I think it was Sailor."

"I never had a pug called Sailor."

Uncle Jack had begun to stiffen; his forehead slid back and he said in his silkiest tone: "Darling, are you doubting my word?"

"I should have thought I might be allowed to know my own dogs. You'll be saying next I don't know my own father."

"Stranger things have happened, my dear."

"What the devil do you mean by that?"

They were off; I had not intended to start a hare but that was what I had done. I went up to bed by the back stairs, leaving them at it. Next morning, Aunt Madge was in one of her sulks. The fit lasted for ten days; and I was none the wiser. A lapse of nearly twenty years might have turned a poodle into a pug in

Aunt Madge's mind. My grandfather had worn a golden key
on his watch-chain, and taken his daughters to foreign parts.
But then, Kate knew of this, and probably had built on it. No
wonder Jesting Pilate had not stayed for an answer—not if he
had been questioning someone like my cousin Kate.

Chapter Twelve

LOOKING back, it seems incredible that any collection of undergraduates should have pursued their ways in such total ignorance of the political issues of the day, and indifference towards them. In 1926 occurred an event which rocked and could have wrecked the nation; it split classes and parties and even families in two and left its mark upon the country for years. No one who read the papers could have been taken by surprise. And yet, to the great majority of students at our university, the General Strike came unheralded and out of a clear blue sky, and was taken in a frivolous spirit quite unmatched to its significance.

No doubt this was a narrow point of view. There was a Labour Club, small in membership but ardent in spirit; announcements of its meetings were pinned to the board and, had I attended any, I should have learnt of the prolonged crisis among the coal-miners that led to the strike, and of the winter-long deliberations of the Samuel Commission whose report, published in March and immediately rejected, precipitated the strike on May 3rd. No doubt the Tories and Liberals had clubs to match, and there was an active debating society. It was just luck, that the people I fell in with lacked interest in politics; but I was by no means the only one to be so ill-informed.

As a result of this political illiteracy, overnight the students became a reservoir of scabs. Not that such a thought crossed our minds. In our own eyes we were patriots answering the call that emerged, with seemly moderation, from primitive and crackling wireless sets, to save the nation from chaos, revolution and ruin. We were doing our bit to keep its life-blood pumping through its arteries: getting milk to children, the sick to hospital, food to the hungry, essential supplies to all who needed them; without us, babies would have died, hospitals been paralysed, banks closed, starvation threatened, violence unleashed and, both literally and figuratively, the lights would have gone out all over Britain.

The people who were trying to bring all this upon the nation, the strikers, were so plainly wicked, or misguided at the best, that no one questioned his duty to defeat them, or his virtue in doing so. That the cause of the miners might have been just, and the strike a gesture of loyalty and self-sacrifice by fellow-workers, was a point of view which, though no doubt subscribed to by the Labour Club, never entered the minds of the rest of us. To be fair, we did not blame the miners either; we knew them to be poor, under-privileged and probably exploited, but blamed their leaders for misleading them. James Cook and Herbert Smith were tools of the Bolsheviks, as the communists were still called, and Bolsheviks, we all knew, were creatures of infinite depravity. Beneath the surface of our carefree lives had festered these sores, threatening to poison the national bloodstream; the least we could do was to rally, in this hour of crisis, to the healers' side.

And for once, the angels, not the devil, had the best tunes. The angels had the trains, trams, lorries and buses that needed to be driven, the signal boxes to be manned, the ships to be unloaded, the undergrounds to be run, the power stations to be operated and practically everything else that was unusual, exciting and, for the time being, invested with glamour. If you had asked a student of botany to unload a shipload of tomatoes, or a history scholar to stoke a locomotive, in the ordinary course of events he would no doubt have indignantly refused. At a place like Reading, most of the botanists and historians had emerged quite recently from the ranks to which dock-hands and stokers also belonged, and to get away as far as possible from such drab, dead-end and ill-paid occupations had been their principal motivating force, or that of their parents.

But this was different: this was saving the nation. For the strike's nine days' duration we lived in an atmosphere of war minus any of its disadvantages. No one was deliberately killed; no bombs, shells or shrapnel fell upon us, no one shivered in rat-infested trenches, no one went homeless or hungry; an occasional tossed stone or abusive picket merely added a mild threat of distant danger; and all the male undergraduates had a wonderful time driving lorries and trains amid an air of adventure, excitement and the utmost good humour. It was astonishing how little went seriously wrong. Cambridge, I think took over the signal boxes at the London termini, and why no accidents resulted, especially as the trains were also in the hands of amateurs, was a mystery only to be solved by the assumption that supposedly skilled jobs such as signalling, engine-driving and the like (and later on could well have been added piloting ships through the Suez Canal) are not nearly as difficult as those who normally discharge them make them out to be.

The women had a much less interesting time. Most of us found our way either to a canteen, or to an emergency head-quarters set up near the railway station where we compiled lists of other volunteers. Here we found plenty of emergency atmosphere, but not enough to do; volunteers appeared in droves and the number of lorries, buses, trams and trains for them to drive was limited. But it was a change from lecture room, laboratory and library. While all was quiet in Reading, you never knew what might happen next, and rumours buzzed about like bees. Voices from wireless sets that boomed, cackled, swelled and often faded away altogether spoke of the army being called in to escort convoys of lorries from the docks, of all leave cancelled, of H.M.S. *Barham* and *Ramillies* recalled from some-where overseas to Merseyside, and of a huge food depot set up in Hyde Park. Pickets and volunteers pelted each other with garden produce; at any moment some wounded hero would return from the battle-front scarred by ripe tomatoes and dripping with egg-yolk, to receive first aid.

The four members of the Philosophers' Club were among the first to volunteer, departing in plus fours and black, white and purple woollen mufflers for the front, if they could find it. Their ambition was to drive trains, but this they did not achieve. Viney, by reason of his O.T.C. experience, had the most exciting job, helping to guard a convoy of lorries taking food from the docks to the Midlands; once or twice the lorries were stoned, and one had to be abandoned when its engine failed, so he had stirring tales to tell, if no actual wounds to show like the heroes of Agincourt. Turner manned a signal box at Didcot. It was easy enough, he said, as there were few trains, and rather boring; he passed the time reading Bulldog Drummond and the romances of Dornford Yates, dipping into Fream's *Elements of Agriculture*, and playing cards. Dando enrolled at the local headquarters of the R.S.P.C.A. and patrolled the station, helping to feed and water any animals that arrived in transit. A surprising number did, including several consignments of pigeons to be posted in strategic positions to man communications, should other forms be sabotaged.

I found myself working in the same room as Swift—if you could call it working; after the rush to volunteer had died down we had virtually nothing to do. We brewed tea or cocoa, knitted gloves and sweaters, and a few of us brought text-books. I asked what Abdul was doing. "He's gone into hiding." "Who's he hiding from?" "I suppose the strikers. He talks about plots and spies and things and goes on at me to bring him food—rice, he wants, but that's impossible." I asked where he was hiding. "In a kind of shed behind the Wesleyan chapel, where they keep teacups and chairs. He's been very odd lately, there's something on his mind." Swift was slapdash in her filing but good at brewing tea, and the retired Brigadier in charge of the office took to putting his head round the door and saying: "Miss Swift, have you a moment, please?" The moments grew longer, and Swift dropped hints of high-level conferences, Ministers on the telephone and mysterious official secrets. "He's quite a pet," she said. I wondered whether Abdul was starving in his shed behind the Wesleyan chapel; if only he had possessed four legs, Dando could have been called in and would almost certainly have provided rice; as a biped, he was beyond her aid.

About half way through, the strike petered out so far as we were concerned; the names of all the volunteers had been registered and filed, rotas established, and everything was ticking over with no one short of anything they really needed, so far as we knew; in the absence of ordinary newspapers we depended on the not very informative *British Gazette* and on news bulletins read to us in impeccable tones by Stuart Hibberd and a corps of assistants who, we understood, wore dinner jackets and boiled shirts before the microphone, thus preserving a proper gentlemanly tone. "Business as usual," our leaders had advised; so faithfully had this advice been followed that, after the first week, it was plain that the strike had failed, and it could be only a matter of days before, in the words of the Prime Minister, "the angel of peace, with healing in his wings, will be among us again; and when he comes, let us be there to meet him." And there, indeed, was Mr. Baldwin in his bowler with his pipe, supported by Sir William Joynson-Hicks in his frock coat, to greet the angel in a dignified fashion and get the nation back to work; while in the columns of the *Daily Express* Strube's Little Man, also in his bowler, emerged from the General Strike Wood mopping his brow and saying "Hello, everybody." Students returned to lab and lecture, swopping tales in the Buttery; it was satisfactory to have had a part, however undramatic, in saving the nation. Most of us felt that some kind of national boil had burst and that a new era of peace, prosperity and pulling-together lay ahead, with Bolsheviks and traitors shown up for what they were and properly discredited.

Most, but not quite all. Labour Club supporters were glum and bitter. While I had no friends among them, I knew slightly one called Nash, and a few days before the strike ended, found myself sitting beside him in the library. We emerged together, and walked along the cloisters. Nash was short, square and stocky, with coarse hair that stood up instead of lying down, and an aggressive, I'm-as-good-as-you-are manner which no doubt was self-defensive, but also putting-off. He was an active member of the dramatic society, and I remembered a recent performance in *Pompey the Great*; he had strutted the boards imperially in a purple toga, half absurd and half impressive, for he spoke the lines ringingly, and the betrayal of a leader who, in his day, had tried to save the nation from a power-hungry Caesar had so engaged his emotions as to add a real punch to his style. So sincere was he that something came across to stamp the performance on the mind, despite the hamish nature of the play, at least as it was put on by amateurs at one end of the assembly hall behind a row of footlights planted on the floor like pumpkins; for we lacked a proper stage.

"What are you rehearsing for now?"

Nash laughed without amusement, a kind of bark.

"Bloody revolution!"

"That's what Churchill says."

"The old bastard's right."

"Then you can't blame the Government for calling out the troops."

"Who's blaming them, love?"

"Well, Ramsay MacDonald and Citrine and so on I suppose."

"Them!" Nash did not actually spit, but gave that impression. "Sodding lot of stuffed shirt bastards. One thing this strike has done, it's showed them up for good and all. Next time it'll be different."

"You ought to get a soap-box," I suggested.

"Don't need one, love. Make myself heard without. Have a coffee, if you'll risk your posh friends cutting you for associating with a proletarian revolutionary."

"I haven't any posh friends."

"All those rugger types."

"What's posh about rugger?"

"I've a couple of seats for the Varsity match at Twickenham if you'd care to join me. After that a spot of supper at the Café de Paris." He was putting on a mock Oxford accent, exaggerated and silly, I thought.

"Are you a miner's son by any chance?" Working-class intellectuals were believed almost always to be miners' sons, perhaps because of D. H. Lawrence.

"I'm bloody well not. If I was, I'd be down the pit doing my bit to see Colonel Lane-Fox got his vintage port and Daimler limousine and slaughtered all those birds in Scotland. Not wasting public money reading Donne and Milton and sounding off at the debating club and preaching bloody revolution and messing about with amateur dramatics. I want to put on *The Emperor Jones* next term."

I could see why Nash would be excited by a play that was virtually a monologue by a paranoic Negro to the accompaniment of tom-toms, ghosts, bangs and hair-raising shrieks, and a diatribe against slavery, but supposed the stagecraft would be difficult—a jungle in the assembly hall, and tom-toms. There were no parts for women.

"D'you know what the club's putting on this term? Barrie! Sir James bloody Barrie! A play about a butler. Waste half a summer messing about with that rubbish!" Nash was a man who made the most of being angry in a proletarian style; you could not imagine him lying back in a punt playing the gramophone.

"You ought to approve of it. The butler comes out on top and shows up his employers."

Nash gave the sort of snort I supposed would be represented in nineteenth-century novels by the word "pshaw", and with infinite contempt spat out the word "butlers!" We walked along the cloisters together; he took long strides, perhaps to make up for the shortness of his legs. This made him look self-important and must agitate the chips that rested so heavily on his shoulders.

"Ever do any hiking?" he inquired.

"Well, not much. I like walking, though."

"Cheap and healthy. Make it pay, too, sometimes."

"Walking? How?"

"Mushrooms for one thing. Sixpence a pound. Early mornings. Come out one morning and we'll go shares."

"There wouldn't be much to share in May."

"What's wrong with May? No R in the month or something?"

Even though England was not my country, I knew that May was not the right time of year for mushrooms. I supposed that he was pulling my leg. "All right," I said. "We'll go mushroom hunting when the strike's over."

"It's over now to all intents and purposes. Thanks to you and your lot. I hope they're satisfied. Because they've dug their own graves."

Before he could start again I left him, almost at the run. This time I was sure he was not pulling my leg. Then how about the mushrooms? Perhaps there *were* some in May? My second year included mycology, so I should find out then.

Meanwhile there was the return of Turner to look forward to, fresh from his signal-box, and Viney from his convoys, Thomas from delivering milk and Corbett from cleaning locomotives in the railway workshops; heroes all, having saved the nation. If no one had run the trains and lorries, people really would have starved, and died because they could not get to hospital; as it was, only the miners were hungry. Obviously they ought not to be hungry, and Nash (as well as Mr. Cook) was right about the coal-owners, who would now be stronger than ever; you could not, apparently, save the nation without saving the coal-owners as well—but you did not save the miners. It was all too difficult for me, and left me uneasy. Nash was like a spike that prodded into tender places and punctured complacency. To most of us the strike was just an episode, exciting for the train-drivers and a change for everybody else; to Nash it was a vision, a portent and a tragedy. In nine days it was over.

Chapter Thirteen

IT was the river that drew us. As soon as you rounded the bend above the gas-works, there it lay: serene, unflurried, half asleep between low green banks bound by willow roots and leaning thorns with secret burrows for the water-voles; beyond stretched the unscarred pastures with their browsing cattle, red and roan, and russet poplars and creamy elder-flowers. Its gentleness fascinated; the Thames is never violent, never threatening, never wild. There is nothing to beware of; the most savage of its creatures is a swan; it harbours no ugly diseases; it does not hurl itself through dangerous rapids nor thunder over falls. It just flows.

As a rule you could not even see it flowing; only twigs, leaves and little bits of flotsam gave it away. The hours remembered were the smiling ones—one in five or six, probably. During the others, you huddled under an awning in your punt, or crouched in a sodden mac in your open sculler, blue with cold, or waited glumly in a boat-house hoping for the drizzle to clear. Nevertheless the river drew us: thither we proceeded on every free afternoon in spring or summer, in boats hired for a shilling an hour. Mixed parties chose punts. The men, always in whites, gave rise to tremendous merriment if they lost the punt-pole or fell in. Girls without escorts generally preferred scullers; if you wanted to explore the river, a twin sculler was the thing. Canoes were for the adventurous bent on nosing up weed-choked backwaters of the Lodden, or on fast travel. On fine afternoons we would moor the boat to a tree-root or branch and lie back and doze and look at the sky and feel the river's ancient tranquillity soak into us: marinaded, so to speak, in its gentleness. When a launch passed the wavelets lapped against the planks, still very gently, with a sound like a faint, good-humoured chuckle.

These were ideal conditions for reading poetry and for making love. We indulged in both; but for love we needed, or thought we needed, more privacy than a punt generally afforded.

Because of the expense at least two couples, if not three, generally shared a punt. (And there was always a gramophone). Scullers were uncomfortable. We searched for backwaters, which were often pre-empted, like parking-places in later years; we had more reticence than our successors—shyness, anyway. Like wisps of mist not quite lifted from the valley, shreds of the myth of Man the Savage Beast still hung about the shoulders of our meek companions; and in the lenses of their spectacles the shade of Diana the Huntress was perhaps momentarily reflected as she drew her bow behind our backs. Still, there were the backwaters, and a long, slow dusk scarfing them with secrecy and stealth, and the whispering water, and swans like blossoms in the darkness, and the warmth of arms, and at last gasometers squat and black against a deep-blue sky. We were not without romance.

Our river-life reached its climax with the Henley regatta. Finals were over, the long vacation just ahead. This was the crown of the year. For the Philosophers' Club, it was an end and a beginning; its members had their degrees and soon would disperse to all quarters of the globe—Corbett to Australia, Viney to Africa, Thomas to New Zealand and Turner to Trinidad. This was the last occasion on which they would be together, for the rest of their lives. They decided to do things in style, and hire a motor launch. I had entertained no hopes of being asked to join the party; Snugg had Turner firmly in tow. To my surprise Viney invited me, in a formal little note.

We started each morning from the boat-yard above Caversham bridge, armed with sandwiches and attired in sleeveless summer dresses and broad-brimmed hats—not cloches for once. The river seethed with eights, fours and darting scullers. The eights looked wonderful: so slim, low and graceful, like arrowheads or spears streaking along just above the water, oars dripping diamonds as they swung back, and slipping into the water like knife-blades into butter. They were engines of motion, those eights, thrusting through the bright air, commanded by a small figure crouching in the stern with a megaphone like a snout on his face. Men in shorts, also with megaphones, trotted or cycled along the tow-path, hoarsely proffering advice. Innumerable small craft were proceeding in the same direction, hugging the banks.

Viney puzzled, alarmed and attracted me. He had none of Turner's easy-goingness and gaiety and charm. He was silent and reserved, and seemed (though he was not) older than the rest of us. His eyes, a dark delphinium-blue, were deepset; his hair, closely cropped, receded from a high forehead; probably in later years he would go bald. He kept his body hard, spare and fit. Socially, you could say that he was dull, yet he was not; it was more that he had built a wall, topped with broken glass like a prison's, to keep out intruders into his privacy. All girls, apparently, were kept out. Although I knew he had invited me merely to square off the numbers, I could not help feeling pleased. It was a small triumph that excited the envy of Snugg, even though she had the prized Turner well, or fairly well, secured.

"I do think you're clever," she remarked, "to find something to talk about to Viney. But then you're used to strong, silent men."

"Am I?" I could recall few. "Why?"

"The colonies are full of them. I'm sure you'll draw him out."

On this intimidating note, which made me think of dressing poultry, we went aboard the launch and chugged off towards Henley, our gramophone at full blast. (Most of them played *Blue Skies* most of the time.) Viney seldom had a pipe out of his mouth or hand, and made great play with filling it, ramming down the tobacco, lighting matches and so forth. He nearly always let the matches burn out before he lit the pipe—a great waste, I thought, of matches, but possibly it saved tobacco; he smoked Three Nuns.

"An odd name for a tobacco," I remarked.

"Why?"

"I don't suppose nuns smoke pipes."

"How do you know what nuns do? They may smoke like chimneys in their cells."

"We've got three nuns taking a special course in chemistry. It looks odd, nuns in habits with their coifs and things sucking hydrochloric acid through a pipette."

"There you are. When they get home they light up to take the taste away."

Conversation with Viney was an exchange of sounds rather than of meanings. You bounced the ball and back it came without making the least dent on the wall around his mind. Over his evening pint, Viney would have forgotten all about the launch and its occupants and anything said there; but he would remember the performances of the various crews and the times they had taken to row the course. Events interested him more than people. Even his favourite sport, long-distance running, was a solitary one. After a few more discouraging attempts I gave up trying to make conversation and we watched the river and its boats and people, a brave and animated scene. The surrounding meadows were starred with daisies, gilded with buttercups—no bungalows then, no caravans, no chemical sprays to obliterate the buttercups; sunlight flecked the water, most of the men were in white and some wore boaters, the women's hats were gay as flowers and many women carried brightly coloured parasols as well. We feared the sun in those days, little though we saw of it—perhaps for that reason, it was a stranger—and erected barriers to keep it off. Coming from a country where the sun *did* shine, I found this queer. Against the rain, those flimsy parasols were useless, and the boats' awnings not much better, for the rain always blew in at an angle. But everyone pretended it was not there, and went on watching the races.

The regatta ended on a Saturday and that evening there was a fair in the meadows; the crews broke their training and it was said to be a wild affair. Women undergraduates were not supposed to go, but many of the bolder spirits did. Swift, of course, was one.

"Come on," she said to me, "for a lark."

I had never been to a fair, so it would be an experience; at this age one collected experiences as one might collect stamps or coins, and hoarded them.

"How shall I get there?"

"Abdul's going to try to raise a car. He wants to study British sports at first hand."

"Are there sports at fairs?"

Swift's hoot almost matched a bulling heifer's. "You bet there are. And I don't mean bowling for coconuts."

It sounded too promising to miss, I asked Dando to unlock the front door after everyone had gone to bed. "I think you're an ass," she said, "I'll unbolt the door for you, but don't blame me if you're caught."

"Of course not. What are you doing in the vac?" This was the time when everyone asked this question, and seldom listened to the answer.

"Oh, home. I may put in a bit of time in a cheese factory at Yeovil."

"I thought you were going to stay with Jumbo."

Dando blushed a deep crimson, it really was crimson, and gazed at the carpet, deprived of speech.

"I'm sure you'll enjoy it." I found myself using a soothing tone, as to a nervous horse. After a short interval she was able to mumble: "Mrs. Mackeson's an awfully good sort."

The car picked me up in the town. It was a battered old snub-bonneted saloon full of people, mostly sitting on each other's laps. I knew none of them except Swift and Abdul, who looked harassed, and had a plump young girl of fifteen or sixteen with bleached blonde hair (twinked, we called it) and a lot of make-up, and wearing garters, more or less on top of him.

"My landlady's daughter," he said.

"Daughter?" Swift queried. "Your landlady's sixty if she's a day."

"Niece," Abdul corrected. The neice gave a squeal. "Whatever's this great lump you've got here," she cried, pummelling his stomach. "Hard as nails and I don't mean—" There were gales of laughter from everyone but Abdul, who tried to shrink away.

"That is private," he protested. "Very private."

The laughter became so uncontrolled that we nearly hit a bus. At the wheel was a youth with a pomade smelling strongly of hair-oil and a very wide pair of Oxford bags.

"There are pickpockets," Abdul said.

"Pickpockets? Where?"

"In public places. This fair, it is a public place. So I take precautions. Leave alone, please." It was no good. He had his money in a leather purse attached to a belt strapped around his plump belly, under his suit. Everyone rolled and writhed, practically insensible with laughter. The evening had started as

a lark and become a scream already; heaven knew how it would
end.

For Abdul, it ended in disaster. Fairs were not his cup of tea.
Dodgems terrified him, swings and roundabouts brought on
nausea and the extraction of pennies from a money-belt proved
a complicated and embarrassing operation. What with the fairground music thumping and blaring away at full blast, the songs
of rowers celebrating victory or drowning sorrows of defeat,
the shouting fairground men, the jostling crowds, it was all
confusing and a little savage; and a good many people were
drunk. Someone was sick over Abdul's brown and white suede
shoes. A kind of rugger scrum developed between supporters of
two rival colleges, which soon embraced a great many young
men; the ball was a policeman's helmet which, in a battered
condition, found its way on to Abdul's head; he was paraded
shoulder-high round the fairground and would have been
dumped in the river had not another party of revellers set upon
the party that was making sport with Abdul, who disappeared
in the fray.

Amid the kaleidoscope of moving faces, Turner's and Viney's
emerged; arm in arm, they were walking among the side-shows
carefully but unsteadily, Turner clasping an object in his spare
hand. He was bare-headed and his hair ruffled; he grinned at me,
and waved the object: a butter dish won at the hoop-la stall.

"Sterling silver. Hall-marked." Viney said.

"Presented," Turner added, "by Napoleon Bonaparte to the
Empress Eugénie."

"The Empress Josephine, I think."

"Eugénie."

"Josephine."

"*M'sieu, je vous en prie—*"

They unlinked arms, faced each other and bowed.

"You have the choice of weapons, M'sieu."

"Pistols. For Eugénie."

"Swords. For Josephine."

"At dawn. Behind the riding school."

They bowed again, and Turner reverently handed me the
hideous little flimsy dish. "For safe keeping. Restore it to the
victor's hand."

"Over the coffee."

"For one." They bowed once more, swaying a little but remaining upright and agreeable; at least they showed no disposition to join impromptu rugger scrums. Inseparable, they appeared. Was there no way to detach Turner? The music, the crowds and laughter, a pulse of excitement in the atmosphere, all these made me feel that I was on the brink of some momentous experience. Here was Turner, and there was the experience, hovering as it were in the air, lurking among the buttercups in the shadows—so close, and yet so inaccessible.

"I came with Swift and Abdul," I said, playing for him. "He's wearing a money-belt with a purse on it round his tummy."

They looked graver than ever. "A ruse," said Viney. "I've long suspected this."

"Suspected what?"

"Stolen plans. In the purse." The sibilants were giving trouble, but he tackled them doggedly. "To be handed to the Ambassador."

They gazed at each other with great solemnity. "We must thwart them," Turner said.

"Certainly. I was very good at thwarting once. I thwarted for my school."

"The illuminated boats are getting ready," I suggested. There was to be a boat parade, with lights attached to masts and awnings. People were drifting from the fairground towards the bank. My companions paid no attention.

"The Ambassador is in disguise," Turner continued.

"Of course. The Bearded Woman?"

"The Fat Lady?"

They nodded at each other in agreement. "Meet us at midnight," Turner said to me, "by the tent of the Fat Lady." He lifted an eyebrow and added: "Guard the butter dish; we shall need it to conceal the plans." They turned in unison and marched off towards a tent labelled Refreshments.

The illuminated boats were dancing on the water as they set forth on their journey through a gentle drizzle and a cold wind. I felt tired and disenchanted, and wished I had not come to such a stupid affair; moreover, I had no idea how to get home. There must be buses. I left the fairground and crossed the bridge towards the town.

People were leaning on the wall to watch the line of boats hung with lanterns moving upstream in a penumbra of shimmering reflection, scattering a cascade of gold over the water. The air was damp against my cheek, my heart was thumping like the fairground tunes; this was not a thing to watch alone, I longed for company and yet I was grateful for the solitude. There was a smell of mud, reeds, tree-roots, river; pale swans with arched necks and angry faces drifted by. Customers were emerging from the Bull, lights streamed across the road, voices joined unsteadily in a dirge-like chant. *"The more we are together, together, together, the more we are together . . ."* Why did people sound so melancholy when they were having a good time? The melancholy of a pub, a bar, the smell of beer . . . Still clasping the butter dish, I walked past the Bull in search of buses and almost bumped into a thickset man with hair sprouting like a stiff broom, clad in a dilapidated macintosh.

"Lost your playmates?" he inquired. "Squiffy, the whole bloody lot. On the scrumpy. I've had enough of this, I'm going home." It was Nash.

"The illuminated boats . . ."

"Illuminated my aunt Fanny. All those swing-together sods, lit up like Christmas candles. Your rowing blue pals."

I wondered why Nash was always so scorpion-like. Creatures sting when they are hurt; what was hurting him? He had made a position for himself, a safe job awaited him. He could not stop acting the part for which he had cast himself. Snugg too, Swift, Viney, even Turner—perhaps everyone was acting and no one could be happy until he had settled on his part and made himself at home in it. The search for the right part, that was what was so confusing.

"All right," Nash said. "Look at the perishing boats if you want to." We walked back to the bridge, but the boats had moved upstream and lost their magic, and the drizzle returned. "I'm going home," Nash repeated.

"So am I, if I can get there. Is there a bus?"

"Aren't any of your posh pals taking you?"

"I do wish you'd stop talking about my posh pals."

Nash gave a bark of laughter. "Gets you on the raw, doesn't it? You know, I can't quite place you."

"Do I have to be placed?"

"You bloody well do. Graded like a bloody bullock in the market, pushed into a pen by blokes with sticks and there you stay till you rot. That's the system. Take it or smash it. It's up to you."

"Yes, I see. Meanwhile, how does one get home?"

"How did you get here?"

"In a car with Swift and Abdul, among others, but I've no idea where they are."

"Abdul? I know where *he* is—in jug."

"Whatever for?"

"Assaulting a copper. Two coppers in fact. One's got a fractured skull and the other half his ribs broken. Pretty good effort for a gippy, if you ask me. I'm going to see what we can do for him tomorrow—legal aid fund, telegrams to M.P.s, questions in the House, that sort of thing."

"I don't believe it. There's been a mistake."

We were walking now beside the river, it seemed to me away from the town. "Is this the right direction for the buses?" But Nash's mind was no longer on buses, his thoughts had excited him, he was striding with his macintosh, much too long, flapping in the wind.

"You know, I could make something of you," he said, suddenly stopping. "In spite of a bloody awful background— colonial, too. You're still malleable."

"Possibly, but what I want now is a bus."

"The first step is to join the club and come to meetings." Nash suddenly stepped forward and put his face close to mine. There was moisture on his stiff hair, his breath smelt beery and all at once that male preening look came over him; the half-parted lips, the shining eye, the turkey-cock spreading his wattles.

"I think I shall give you some private tuition."

"You take too much for granted."

He had an arm round me now. "What's that you've got in your hand?"

"A butter dish."

"You won't need that now." Before I knew what was hap- pening he had seized the butter dish and hurled it into the river—or at least towards the river; it was a bad throw and the wretched little piece of metal bounced off the wharf with a clatter and disappeared, whether into the water or into one of the boats moored to the wharf I never knew. A boat-house loomed blackly behind us; we had halted by a boat-hiring yard.

"Come on, lass," he said, enfolding me tightly. "No bob an hour a boat this time of night."

So dreams among the buttercups became reality among the tethered boats whose cushions had been locked away for the night; I was left without the butter dish but with subsequent bruises, luckily in invisible places. I was not in the least in love with him but he had experience and clever hands and, being unprepared for this, did not proceed to its ultimate conclusion, though he got as near to it as safety permitted.

So, after all, experience did not prove a dupe, although it had sneaked up casually and unannounced from an unexpected direction. Nash put me on a bus, but did not escort me back to Reading. The fair went on.

It was a day or two before I saw Swift. "Sorry we missed each other on Saturday," she said. "There was a bit of a gafuffle over Abdul."

"So I heard."

"He had a bobby's helmet on and so he was arrested. When the Dean went to bail him out next day his passport wasn't in order or something, so they wouldn't let him go."

"Is he still in prison?"

"I don't know where he is now. Probably deported. They seemed to think he was a spy."

"He didn't seem like one."

"No, but then spies mustn't seem like spies, must they? By the way, Turner was looking for you."

"Turner was? When?"

"At the fair. He was nattering about butter dishes and a Fat Lady and a date with you at midnight. Said he waited, but you didn't turn up. He was pretty squiffy."

"Oh."

"So we joined forces. Hot stuff, is Turner. Quite a lad."

"I daresay."

"Even old Viney got lit up. It was quite an evening. Sorry

I shan't be here for next year's Henley. Well, have a good vac."
   "Same to you."
   That was the last I saw of Swift. Years later, I heard she had married and gone to Canada, but never learnt what became of her there. I expect she got by.

Chapter Fourteen

"HAVE you seen your uncle Alex lately?" Gertrude asked. "I haven't seen him at all."

"He wants to give you a horse."

"A horse?"

"Yes. He's made some money suddenly, something very fortunate he said. It may have been *on* a horse."

"It's awfully kind of him. But I don't quite see . . ."

Gertrude was paying one of her brief visits to Nathan's Orchard to wash and iron, and I was there for part of the vacation. Gertrude, it seemed, had met my half-uncle at one of her country-house parties.

"What would the horse be for?" I asked.

"To hunt on, I should imagine."

"I couldn't hunt at Reading."

"Ralph hunted at Oxford."

"Reading isn't Oxford. Besides, a horse must cost a lot to keep."

"You'd better explain that to Alex. He's rather a pet."

"I'm sure he must be. Actually, I don't really *want* a horse."

"Perhaps he'd get you something else instead. What *do* you want?"

"I want to go to America."

Everybody, at that time, wanted to go to America. It was a magnet, a lodestar, a beacon. Everything that was new, peculiar and exciting came out of the West. This belief had been created largely by the cinema. We scarcely ever saw a film that was not American, and the impact was terrific. It was by no means altogether a favourable or enticing impact. In some aspects it was harsh and ugly, but it was never indecisive. Here was another world: could it really be true, or had someone invented it? Those of us endowed, or cursed, with curiosity, wanted to find out. To some extent this corresponded to the feeling that Americans had about Paris, which drew them, excited them, had the aura of the fabulous. But my English contemporaries were not interested in Paris. We knew it had the best food, the best fashions, an elegance and arrogance we may have envied, but in a sense it was *vieux jeu*. It belonged to our parents, to Edward VII and the *entente cordiale* and to history that was over; the history that was to come belonged to the United States.

That was what we dimly thought, anyway. We felt ourselves superior to America and yet in its thrall, as if we were creatures upon whom the juggernaut was advancing to the wail of saxophones, the frenzy of the Black Bottom, the volleys of sawn-off shotguns of Chicago gangsters, the lawlessness of speakeasies, the lyrics of Cole Porter, the plays of O'Neill. America had everything in it that was generous and noble, and everything in it that was vicious and corrupt. The point was, it went to extremes: and we were tired of compromise, of safety-first and bowlered Baldwin. America was like some vast conjuror's top-hat, forever yielding rabbits, bunches of artificial flowers, goldfish, yards and yards of knotted silk scarves and white mice.

"You'd better tell Alex," Gertie said. "He seems to want to do something for you, I don't know why."

I did not know either; I was his only niece, and perhaps he had a sense of duty, or perhaps a generous nature and wanted, in the words of one of our favourite songs, to spread a little happiness as he went by.

So I entered into correspondence with Uncle Alex—we never did meet—and subsequently with various American universities. If you wanted to see America, there could be no better place to start than the campus of one of its colleges. Far-flung bursars responded with packets of catalogues—these had some more academic name—outlining conditions, courses and fees. The fees were low; a one-way trans-Atlantic passage, tourist class, was around £20; it seemed quite feasible to get there and back, and have a year's instruction, for the price of a single hunter, provided it was a reasonably good one, and Uncle Alex always thought in terms of the best.

"Barbarians," Aunt Madge said tersely. "They live in hot-houses on ice-cream and say pardon. No wonder their complexions are like sandpaper. Yours will be the same." Everyone called Americans Yanks—they had brought that on themselves by one of their war songs—and there was a lot of sensitiveness about the debt; the sums we had borrowed from them had been spent on prosecuting the war to make the world safe for democracy, and the Americans' insistence on getting some of it back was considered most ungentlemanly. In cartoons, Uncle Sam was always depicted sitting on a money-bag or with a dollar sign somewhere in the picture. President Coolidge was in the White House, and all that was known about him was the story recounting how he heard a sermon on sin and told his wife that the parson was against it. The only other character we knew about was Big Bill Thompson, Chicago's mayor, who had a feud against King George V, evidently confused in his mind with King George III.

Uncle Jack was troubled about the State of Maine, which had been treacherously filched, in his opinion, from the Canadians, and he was keenly looking forward to a war to put matters right. "Two divisions of British troops," he pronounced with flashing eye and bristling moustache, "would sweep the entire Yankee army into the Potomac!" When I mentioned the Statue of Liberty, his eyes flashed even more. "Please God, within two years we shall have blown it into the sea!"

"People sit for weeks on end on top of flagpoles, and if you have a cocktail you go blind," my aunt added. Evidently I was in for a stirring time. On the other hand there was *Babbitt*, generally conceded to give a true account and certainly a different one; so what to believe? See for yourself was the only answer.

While tourism, as we all know, has lately burgeoned like a science-fiction vine, even in 1927, when I crossed the Atlantic, it was a sturdy plant. The vessel was so crammed that people were sleeping in alley-ways and saloons. Most were returning from a three or four weeks' vacation in France and Italy; only the hardiest had ventured into Britain, where culture took the shape of castles, churches and cathedrals, all chilly places hard on the feet and, after a few days, lowering to the spirits. My fellow travellers were polite about it, but to them England was clearly a duty rather than a pleasure, peopled by natives with no conversation and strange habits, such as bringing hot water into bedrooms in jugs, riding bicycles and walking, instead of riding, up and down stairs. Ours was a land not only with no future but with no present either: only the feudal, ceremonial and unscrupulous past.

Intermingled with returning tourists was a sprinkling of expatriates. This was their age: the age of Midwestern artists searching the Left Bank for the light the Impressionists had found there; of the "babes in the Bois", of the young writers on the *Paris Herald*, where so many chroniclers of Europe's future disintegration learnt their craft; of Iowans who could exist no longer out of reach of the Café du Dôme and of New Yorkers who bought tumble-down villas for a song on the Côte des Maures, and passed long days playing *boule* with local fishermen, drinking in drowsy cafés where strings of beads hung down over doorways, and painting or sculpting a little now and then. Hemingway was writing *The Sun Also Rises* in Paris, Gertrude Stein was there, Cornelia Otis Skinner, Scott Fitzgerald, many others. In my vessel were some of the lesser fry homeward bound in disillusionment. Or so they said; probably the truth was their money had run out, for they displayed no enthusiasm whatever for their native land, and shared the Nathan's Orchard view of my resolve to see it.

"Why America? You've nothing to learn from us. You've the best government in the world. You have more beauty in one village than we have in our whole continent." Mary Curtin said this: she was a widow who had come to paint in Paris, found her talents fell short of her ambition, and was retreating to her native Brooklyn.

"Villages belong to the past. In the future . . ."

"How can the future be worthwhile when it's all so flat? Everything the same from the Atlantic to the Pacific—the cities are the same, the clothes, conversation, food, houses, customs. Even the stories. We've stewed ourselves in the juice of equality. You'll be bored to death in a month."

It was bad for any Briton to be told this, for we were steeped in complacency and arrogance as it was. It is hard to credit what a good opinion we had of ourselves in those days. There was the Empire, and there were we at the heart and centre of the world. No one questioned our position. Everyone else was a barbarian, more or less. Yanks had the effrontery to use our language, and then not even use it correctly—that is, in exactly the same way as we did. In a Frenchman, this was comic; in an American, impudence. Visiting Englishmen brought back samples of American slang jotted down in notebooks, much as anthropologists might return from Borneo with details of curious marriage rites. It was a wonder they were not lynched.

Even I, an obscure twenty-year-old student of agriculture, felt in my heart of hearts that I was honouring the Yanks by wishing to spend a year in their country. Any idea they expressed, or custom they followed, that was not exactly the same as ours, appeared to me comic, naïve or deplorable, or all three. There was, for example, the matter of class. As a colonial myself, pitchforked into it, I had at first found the system complicated, obscure and objectionable, and felt at sea, but by now the prudery and reticence with which the whole subject was cloaked had stifled most of my rebellious instincts, and I was shocked, in my turn, by the American attitude, and even more by their frankness in expressing it.

We treated class as our grandparents, so we were told, had treated sex: while practising it with vigour, pretending it did not exist, and concealing any overt signs of it as something else. Americans had classes like everyone else but based them openly on money and admitted their existence, instead of basing them on derivatives of money, such as education, and bringing in the Deity; God having decided in advance, like a butcher grading meat, which class you belonged to, it became morally wrong as well as socially dangerous to question the system, and almost as difficult to change your class as to change your sex, though both occasionally occurred.

You did not talk about it, however. Mary Curtin did. An Englishman on board was paying her advances, and she did not quite know where he belonged. I did not either; it is hard when you see people out of their context; his accent was public school, so far as I could tell, with a slightly suspicious diphthong intruding now and then; he might not be entirely safe on brown cows. His manner passed muster: or was he, perhaps, a trifle over-polite? His occupation did not help much; he said he had an artificial flower factory in Essex; anyone might have that, from an old Etonian to a Borstal boy.

11

"I'd be glad to invite him out to my apartment," Mrs. Curtin said, "but I'm in a spot. Frankly, honey, I'm a snob; I wouldn't want to ask a *lower-class* Englishman; now you're English, you can tell me where he belongs and then I'll know what to do."

"It isn't quite as simple as that."

"Why wouldn't it be simple? He's English, isn't he? He must be upper class, middle class or lower class. Of course I know there may be border-line cases. He isn't lower class, surely?"

"Somewhere in the middle, I should think. But I'm not an expert."

"You don't have to be an expert if you're English, it's in the blood. My husband was distantly related to the Duke of Manchester. He knew at once where any Englishman fitted in. Do you imagine Roger might be related to a Duke?"

"I suppose anyone might. But one can't ask."

"That's just my difficulty." She patted my knee. "You find out for me, honey. He's kind of cute, but I don't want to encourage anyone my husband wouldn't have cared for. A woman travelling by herself can be deceived." I was shocked by Mary Curtin's candour, and unable to set her mind at rest.

So successful were the homeward-bound expatriates in running down their country, and assuring me that no Britisher would be able to stand it for more than a month, that I was quite unprepared for the beauty of New York. Approached from the sea, it had all those qualities of fable and illusion I had previously imagined it to have. Towers, spires, gleaming pillars pierced a pinkish mist to stab a tender sky: ethereal, fairy-like, here was a dream solidified, a symbol; man groping up to heaven with his concrete fingers, waiting for the touch of God's hand that might one day reach down. There was nothing mean or squalid about these towers that dwarfed the towers of Ilium, at least seen through a pinkish mist of early morning on a fine September day.

I did not expect the customs sheds, docks, subway and the streets of Brooklyn to sustain the illusion, but even Brooklyn was not as bad as everyone had told me it would be. Mary Curtin had invited me—taking a chance, I supposed, on my class, which mattered less in a girl than in a man—to spend the night in her apartment, which she shared with a daughter who worked in a museum. The daughter was small, neat, gay and very pretty, the apartment had some decorative Chinese porcelain and Moorish pottery, it was simply and cleverly furnished, and we had an excellent light meal. Both Curtins went to endless trouble to make me feel at home. If this was the land of the barbarians, at least the civilized were getting their due.

New York, to me, was a city; I knew from the map it was also a State, but had never imagined how large a State, or how beautiful. I was lucky to see it for the first time in the fall, with all the woods aflame: great sheets of flaming crimson stretching from one hilltop to another up the craggy valleys and, when I reached my destination, all around the finger lakes of Ithaca. It was romantic to be going to Ithaca, whose name evoked Homeric legends, the image of Penelope with her tapestry and suitors, and wine-dark seas. No wine-dark sea, however splendid, could have been more splendid than those flaming maples, which did not always turn red; some were golden, and when you walked under them, and on a bed of rustling yellow leaves, you walked through a tunnel of limpid gold that might have been a street in paradise.

I could not see all this, however, when I arrived in Ithaca, for it was late at night. During a nine-hour journey in the big, rushing train with its Negro attendants, panic had invaded my bowels. I knew no one in Ithaca, indeed in North America, and nothing whatever about the university in which I had so precipitately enrolled; everything was large and rough and frightening, unfinished-looking, the people foreign, their language strange. The impulse that had led me here now seemed insane, the whole enterprise doomed to ghastly failure, and I would gladly have sold my soul to the devil to get back to Nathan's Orchard or to Reading, and the people I knew.

I stood on the platform with my grips. Doors slammed, the locomotive chuffed, the big train rattled into the night, from a distant darkness came the mournful toll of its bell. Two girls appeared, and greeted me so warmly that I wondered whether they were not old friends I had forgotten about, turned up unexpectedly. They led me to a trolley-car which clambered up an almost perpendicular hill, lurching round one hairpin bend after

another, until the lights of the town sparkled far below. Whither
were we bound?

"Prudence Risley."

"Who is she?"

The girls tinkled; the laughs of nearly all college girls, I soon
discovered, were tinkles; very few snorted, chortled, hiccuped
or guffawed.

"Why, a girl's dormitory."

A dormitory: rows of beds, packed together, lockers, bells
and orders, like a barrack or school; things looked blacker than
ever and my bowels squirmed. Prudence Risley was not like that
at all. It was a huge building with a central tower copied from
Hampton Court, and a dining room modelled on that of Christ
Church, Oxford. Most girls had their own bedsitters; some
shared, but never more than two. I had a room to myself. It was
all very clean and tidy. No smoking was allowed indoors.

Although midnight was past, the president of Risley met me:
a fourth-year student, Midge by name and rather like one: small,
precise and deft in movement, but also firm and purposeful
beneath a soft exterior, charged with energy to the tip of each
unruffled hair. Her ambition, I later discovered, was to become
an Ambassador, and the mother of ten. She tinkled like the rest
and led me to gatherings of girls who greeted me with overflowing warmth and yet a curious formality, shaking hands and
addressing me by my first name. Just as at Reading you scarcely
knew the first name of your friends, here it was not until you
were on fairly close terms with a fellow coed that you knew her
last one.

Greetings continued for nearly two hours. We had cocoa,
everyone said how glad she was to know me and how she hoped
I would enjoy Cornell and how happy everyone was to have me
with them. It was all very strange. In England, you slid unob-
trusively into the stream of life and no one minded if you sank
or swam; it was your own affair. If you sank, you drowned.
Here, nothing was done without ceremony and people were on
hand to buoy you up; but the current sucked more strongly
towards sharper rocks and fiercer rapids. For the first time it
was borne in on me that Americans were not just rather comic
English people who had developed, with their accent, a number

of peculiar ways, but real foreigners, like Turks or Germans. Our common tongue was less a bond than a mask to conceal the true visage—a deceiver. Later on, I noted down an observation made by a French minister to Washington at the time of Thomas Jefferson: "An American is the born enemy of all European peoples." They swaddled their enemies with love.

At eight o'clock next morning I was called for by a coed who said she was my grandmother. Each female newcomer was allotted a grandmother to guide her through the labyrinth of registration, another process bearing no resemblance to anything I had known at Reading. Whether because of life's greater complexities, or because people had nicer natures, students helped each other much more at Cornell than at Reading. Fourth year students did not look down on freshmen in the absurd English fashion of the day, nor were coeds tolerated only with disdain. Everyone was friendly, at least to one's face; and the face, after all, is the part that matters.

Instead of Reading's eight hundred students, Cornell had over five thousand, and instead of a few simple faculties, a catalogue listing several hundred courses; from this, each freshman selected those he fancied and blended them, as a pharmacist might make up a prescription. It was a complex system, based on credits. Each course carried anywhere from one to four credits, according to the number of lectures it involved each week. The minimum number of credits was sixteen, and students were not encouraged to have more than eighteen, so the range was narrow; also, courses often overlapped. To make up a balanced course was therefore difficult, and involved filling in a great many forms in different offices. Everything was run more like a business than a university, and the blending of courses led to some curious results. While a conscientious freshman put the academic value of the courses he selected above their points value, many had been drawn to the university for less noble reasons than a love of learning. If sixteen hours was the minimum number of credits, sixteen it would be. If, after compiling a suitable time-table, one hour's credit remained unfilled, it was necessary to select a course carrying one hour's credit, no more. Such courses were rare. A professor who conducted one in Medieval Flemish Art was disconcerted, at the start of the

semester, to discover several hundred students trying to crowd
into a lecture-room designed to accommodate about twenty.
One-point courses on the Design of Playing Fields and on the
Structure of Snowflakes also enjoyed an unexpected popularity.

Longer courses covered everything under the sun. You could
sign up for the Arrangement of Cut Flowers, Dalcrose Euryth-
mics, Systematic Olericulture, Horse-Shoeing or Advanced
Truck Crops. It was agonizing to be able to select, out of all
this richness, no more than four or five topics: I felt like a bee
happening upon fields red with clover, forests of lime trees in
bloom, mountainsides of heather, and able to fill its tiny sacs
with honey drawn from no more than half a dozen florets. You
did not even have to stick exclusively to your own faculty.
Although enrolled in the school of agriculture, I could embark
on a course in Greek philosophy, Freudian psychology, French
nineteenth-century novelists, Hindu theology, the structure of
the atom, crystallography, spiritualism, the history of the Incas,
the origin of corals, the genetics of the fruit-fly—I think it
would have been impossible to find a subject ignored at Cornell.

Guidance was provided through the maze. I found myself
consulting a young professor who went to infinite trouble to
find out my needs and inclinations; friendly, unhurried, understanding, he was another new experience. Between us we
settled for a mixed bag embracing Animal Nutrition, Crop Pro-
duction, News Writing, Marketing and Rural Sociology,
reluctantly jettisoning Land Economics, Agronomy II, Micro-
biology, Comparative Literature, Greek Drama, Latin American Art and Ornithology.

Sixteen hours of lectures weekly did not sound a lot, on
average less than three hours a day, but the lecture was the
least part of it. The whole approach was quite different from
that of Reading. For each course there was a list of books you
had to read, and home-work was given. "Read pages 51 to 55
for next time and know it thoroughly." As like as not you
might find on your desk a mimeographed paper with forty or
fifty questions to be answered, each with a bare "yes" or "no",
or a statistic; this was a prelim, an examination given without
warning. It was a memory test and had nothing to do with
university education as I understood it. In England, you would

select perhaps three questions out of six or eight and devote three hours to advancing such opinions and arguments as you could muster, buttressing them with the views of authorities. Examiners at Cornell were seldom interested in undergraduate opinions. Ours not to reason why, ours to absorb a mass of facts and regurgitate them correctly. Facts were black and white, not grey. The fuzziness had gone. The English ambiguity had annoyed me, but now I missed it, and grew impatient with facts I had to memorize although they could all be looked up in books. The aim here was to answer questions; there, to ask them.

It was much harder work at Cornell. You had to concentrate, you had to study, you could not fritter away your time in punts, had there been any, or in Butteries and cinemas, or in just doing nothing. If you failed—busted out—you were rusticated for a semester. (The academic year had two semesters.) Life was real and life was earnest with little time to dream, to idle, to pose, to speculate; and none at all to breakfast at eleven off champagne, or polish off your luncheon with port at four o'clock. Not that we had done such dashing things at Reading but we had lived, more than I had realized, in the long shadow, however thin and flickering by the time it reached biscuit factory and gas-works, of Oxford. No such shadow fell here. We came to study, to learn how to concentrate, and to qualify for a job.

No one could have been kinder, more conscientious and more resolute in helping us towards this goal than the academic staff; they were devoid of that indifference and off-handed aloofness displayed by those British academics who care more for advancing their own reputations than for instructing their pupils. Cornell's professors and lecturers were infinitely more approachable than any I had come across at Reading. But their classes were too large and the syllabus too rigid. They had to stick closely to their guns and keep those guns trained on the target. Numbers overwhelmed them; with so many students, to give each one individual attention was impossible. They were really crammers. For the student, marks were everything. We were on the assembly line.

Yet, having said that, it was paradoxically true that I enjoyed closer personal contacts with several professors and lecturers at Cornell than I ever had at Reading, where I was never once invited into a professor's home. I had not been a week in Ithaca before Professor Bristow Adams invited me to coffee; after that, I had an open invitation to go any Monday evening to his home, where sometimes a dozen others would be gathered, sometimes only two or three, together with his wife and a family ranging from a mother-in-law of over eighty who, as a girl, had trekked Westwards in a covered wagon along the Oregon Trail, to a son in high school. Talk never flagged. Bristow Adams held a Chair of Journalism. He had a dry manner, a grey moustache, a twinkle in his eye and a great flow of conversation on any topic ever raised, but he never lost his calm or spoke with malice. I learnt more at these sessions than in all my courses combined—more, at least, of what I had come to seek, not facts but fancies, not statistics but ideas.

Chapter Fifteen

I HAD been about a week at Cornell when I found a number of gilt-edged invitation cards pushed under the door of my room. Each one requested my company at a rushing party, and they came from places, things or people of whom I had never heard: Kappa Alpha Theta, Delta Delta Delta, Alpha Omicron Pi, Alpha Phi. I took these to my grandmother and asked her what they were.

"Why, invitations to rushing parties."

"Yes, I can see that. What's a rushing party?"

She looked at me in amazement. "You don't have rushing parties in England?"

"I've never heard of any."

"Or sororities?"

"What is a sorority?"

Alarm, as well as amazement, now began to show in Billie's manner. Yet she was not a girl prone to alarm. I had found her friendly, forthcoming and likeable; in about five minutes she had outlined her life-history, hopes, intentions and probable destiny, thus providing a foundation for our future relations which would avoid misunderstanding, much as, at meetings and parties, people sometimes wore labels inscribed with their names on their chests.

Billie was a third-year student majoring in economics. She came from Indiana, where her father was a doctor and raised corn, she was engaged to a boy called Bob who was studying civil engineering at McGill, and her hobby was music; she disliked babies, a reaction which she feared was unnatural, and she feared also that Bob would want to embark upon a whole set of them as soon as they were married; this bothered her sometimes, but she found her ukelele a solace. Now my ignorance of sororities bothered her too.

"I can't go to all these parties," I pointed out. I had nine cards, and the parties were concentrated into one week, so, even if I went out every evening, there would be time for only six. "Which should I accept?"

Billie's embarrassment grew. "I can't advise you about that. I'm breaking all the rules by talking to you now."

"What rules?"

She quoted them. "From the time of arrival in Ithaca until Pledging Day, there shall exist no Natural Intercourse between sorority and entering girls."

"Natural Intercourse . . . ?"

"No calling. No entertaining. No voluntary conversation. No initiative of any kind on the part of a sorority girl towards an entering girl."

"And I'm an entering girl?"

"Surely."

"But you're my grandmother. Can't you help?"

She shook her head. "I'm sorry, honey. You must ask a non-sorority girl."

I showed my cards to a neighbour on my landing at Prudence Risley, a girl called Anna, who had befriended me. The invitations, she said, came from secret societies, although there was little about them that was secret apart from their initiation ceremony. The rushing season lasted for three weeks: busy weeks for everyone, and hedged about with complicated rules.

The whole social life of the campus, it appeared, was centred on fraternities among men, and the corresponding sororities. Each community had its own house, in which resided as many of its members as could be crammed in. The fraternity houses were like small-scale colleges, but had nothing to do with the authorities; they ran their own affairs, elected their officers, employed their staff and supported themselves by means of subscriptions and an initiation fee varying in size according to the status and ambition of the chapter. Each fraternity was a national body, having chapters in colleges from California to Florida, Maine to New Mexico, and chapters for alumnae in all the principal cities of the United States.

Rushing was their reproductive mechanism. It was well named. At the start of each academic year, there was a wild rush by all the frats—between thirty and forty at Cornell, and about fifteen sororities—to woo the more desirable frosh.

Desirability was complex and subtle. It could rest squarely on riches—any son of the president of General Motors or Standard Oil would be desirable in the extreme. Other qualities in the father might reflect desirability upon the son: the offspring of a distinguished senator or scientist, physician or actor, socialite or athlete, would be rushed by the best frats. Otherwise, it was a gamble on the fortunes and talents of the newcomers. Who would become the future captain of football, stroke of the crew, president of the Student Council, editor of the *Sun*, star of the basket-ball team, champion of athletics? Or even, on a lower level, worthy of election to Phi Beta Kappa, the egg-head society? Powers of divination were needed to pick winners, and mistakes naturally made on both sides; once initiation was over, there could be no divorce. On the whole, however, it was remarkable how successfully like called to like. Moreover frosh were malleable, and fraternities applied a powerful pressure that shaped them to the pattern of the group they joined.

There was, of course, a pecking order among the frats. At the top were two or three to which everyone aspired; at the bottom, a layer into which the rejects sank. Selection was a two-way traffic and some students turned down bids from inferior frats if the best ones failed to invite them. Some freshmen got no bids at all. This was a very real disaster, imprinting the stigma of social rejection and all that this implied. Not to be rushed was to be excluded from the herd. Thereafter, for the whole four years of college, you would carry the brand of being not-wanted, of failing to make the grade. Social halitosis of the worst kind. It was a cruel system, crueller than our British class system which so offended most Americans, because it was consciously applied and even more rigid. It had caused student suicides.

Since Anna belonged to no sorority, we could have Natural Intercourse, apparently another name for conversation. She was an attractive and vivacious girl and I wondered why she had remained outside the pale. "I didn't get bids from the sororities I wanted," she explained, "and I didn't care to join the ones that rushed me. So I stayed outside. I guess I've missed something, but I don't mind." She did mind, though, if not to the extent of committing suicide. She picked out five cards from my batch. "These are the ones, honey. The others don't amount to a thing."

Later, I visited Anna's home several times; it was not far from Ithaca, a small farm. Anna's father was a German immigrant and spoke broken, guttural English I found hard to understand. His was the typical American story: penniless arrival, work as a hired hand, frugal living, self-denial, every cent put by until enough had been accumulated to buy a place of his own. There it lay, in a fold of the hills: pasture-land with a small dairy herd, an orchard, and a melon-patch guarded all night with loaded shotguns by Anna's father or her brothers, when the fruit was ripening, against raiders who came out from the cities in trucks.

The wooden house was small, square, in need of paint and totally graceless, dwarfed by a big red wooden barn—all the barns were painted a brownish red, the colour of dried blood—behind it. By the gate stood a receptacle for letters perched on a post like a lost nesting-box, and constantly replenished with mail-order catalogues. Domestic life centred on the porch, in our terms the veranda, with its battered rocking chairs. The house seemed to be full of brothers: stocky, stiff, solemn youths with hair standing up off their foreheads and an air of stolid indifference. They had strong, calloused hands and the heavy tread of farmers, and looked so Teutonic it was a surprise to hear them speak without a German accent.

And there was Anna, German-looking perhaps with her blonde hair and high complexion, yet in all other ways, an American cuckoo in this Teutonic nest: slim, smartly-dressed, high-heeled, talkative, perfectly at ease; she had passed over from the world of liverwurst and dumpfel paste to that of the hot dog and banana split. It was touching to see her father's pride and her mother's solicitude; yet underneath I sensed in them a kind of frustration. Anna had worked out just as they had hoped and planned; she had done well in high school, made the grade to college, she would graduate, marry a college boy, become a true American; and in the process she had passed out of their reach. They could never become true Americans, though they tried hard enough; it was something you were born, not made.

As for Anna, she lived several lives at once. She studied conscientiously, and got good marks; she earned her keep at Prudence Risley as an expert waitress, able to slide with great agility through swing doors, a full tray balanced in one hand above her head and fixed smile on her heart-shaped face; she was well dated up, to be seen with a 'coon-coated escort at every football game; she was on the basket-ball team. Yet the best sororities had not rushed her. Why? Had the shadow of the German immigrant, the stiff-haired brothers and the melon-patch dimmed the brightness of her path, despite all protestations about equality? Britons often said complacently that Americans were even more snobbish than the English. I did not think this true, except perhaps among a small circle of eastern seaboard families listed, or hoping to be listed, in the Social Register; but of course this was a stratified society, although the stratifications were different from our own and I never really understood them. Religion, for example, played a large part. That Anna was a Catholic may have weighed in the scale as much as her first-generation background. There were frats that favoured Catholics and others that would not admit them. Jews were apart. Cornell had two sorority chapters for Jewish girls; none of the others would rush them.

During the first week of rushing I went to a party every evening and they merged in memory into a blur of tidy, polished rooms hung with Japanese lanterns and crammed with tidy, polished girls, every hair in place on neatly trimmed heads, silk-clad and smiling, sweet and warm and eager; smiling, smiling all the time, smiling and tinkling; a smell of incense, the crooning of victrolas, rickety little tables spread with snacks; of crisp, chilled salads with nuts and chunks of pineapple, sweet, soft, cold drinks and excellent hot coffee; of bridge and talk, talk and bridge, and now and then an act with girls dressed in Japanese kimonos, or in top-hats and tails like vaudeville performers.

"So you come from England? Isn't that *exciting*."

At the start I had mentioned Africa, but this was a mistake; people looked blank, startled or incredulous, at a loss for the correct response. One girl made a bold attempt.

"My, my, you must be *courageous* . . ."

"Courageous?"

"I'd be dead scared of all those heifers!"

"But heifers aren't savage as a rule."

"So big and black! With whatsit, assegais . . ." I supposed she meant Kaffirs. It was too complicated, so I let England ride after that.

"Those cute policemen! We went to Windsor Castle and saw the beefeaters . . ."

"And how do you like Cornell?"

"I'd like you to meet our president, I know you'll like her."

"Aren't these programmes *cute*? One of our sisters made them, she's an industrial designer in New York."

"So you're from England. And how do you like Cornell?"

Kindness, consideration, warmth, politeness above all. Everyone was polite. Everything tasted, smelt, felt like honey-dew. The very walls seemed to drip with honey-dew. The cream of paradise . . . And, beneath it all, judgments, hard and shrewd and merciless, were being formed, appraisals made. When the last of us had left, varnished thumb-nails would be turned down on two out of every three of the night's guests.

At last the president gave a signal; we stood up gravely; smiles faded; a religious hush fell upon the room. Someone struck a chord on a piano. In unison, we sang:

> When the sun fades far away
>   In the crimson of the west,
> And the voices of the day
>   Murmur low and sink to rest;
>
> Music with the twilight falls
>   O'er the dreaming lake and dell;
> 'Tis an echo from the walls
>   Of our own, our fair Cornell.

Then home to Prudence Risley under icy stars: clearer, harder, brighter, from the crest of this windswept hill high above Cayuga's waters, than in the old world; home along avenues where fallen leaves rustled underfoot.

By the end of the first week I should have formed a clearcut impression of each sorority, and know to which group of sisters I would prefer, should I be invited, to pledge my life-long allegiance. But they were hopelessly mixed up in my mind. I could not for the life of me recall whether Fran was the girl with orangy lipstick who had made a little slam at Sigma Delta Chi, or the one at Kappa Alpha Theta who had done high kicks and splits with such spirit, ending with cartwheels. At one party they had proffered excellent little *vol-au-vents* with shrimp fillings, at another a particularly luscious walnut layer cake; but that was clearly not the basis for life-long loyalty. Anna's advice was negative. One of the sororities had a higher snob rating than the others, there were some very lovely girls among its members, but it also had a higher initiation fee. Another was more eclectic, and had a lot of sisters prominent in Activities. There was a wide choice of these, each offering an avenue to that distinction and success which all sought with unremitting energy, in order to peg out a bit of territory of their very own amid the herd.

You might go in for sports; for coeds there was tennis, rowing, basket-ball and shooting on a miniature range, pursued in very baggy red bloomers, like those worn by lady cyclists in the 'nineties. You might go in for Student Government and belong to one, or more, of a network of committees covering every field of campus life. Election to office counted as an honour, and was put after your name in the campus register. People collected honours as ambitious soldiers collect medals. Then there was debating, acting, music, photography, all the usual things. Almost everyone could shine at something, and so gain a little self-esteem.

At the start of the second week of rushing, another batch of invitations arrived, but fewer, and you were not supposed to accept more than three. During the third and final week you went to only two—formal dinner parties this time, in evening dress. Then you must decide. By this time the serious nature of your choice had been borne in upon you by all the gatherings and pressures and songs, and by the semi-mystical attitude of your sisters-to-be, to whom their sorority was much more than just a group of girls who shared a house for convenience' sake and were supposed to be congenial. It had some of the mystique of a religious order. The sisters, it was true, did not include chastity among their vows, but they did include reverence for the ideals of the sorority and obedience to its rules. A sorority had ideals, it had a ritual and insignia like the Masons, by which an initiate must pledge her faith and dedicate her talents. A bond deeper than that of ordinary friendship was believed to unite her with her sisters not only on the campus here and now, but throughout the country and for the rest of her life. This was not a matter to be taken lightly, and no one did take it lightly. To be pledged was a solemn affair.

So solemn, that at the last moment I had doubts. Girls like Anna, who did not belong, said that by joining you surrendered your freedom to choose your own friends and be chosen by them. You had a ready-made set, and must abide by these. While it was not actually forbidden to make friends with members of other frats, it did not often happen, no doubt partly for practical reasons, much as boys at the larger English public schools seldom make close friends with boys from other houses because opportunities to see much of them are few. But there was rather more to it than that. "They watch you," Anna said. "If you act in some way they don't approve, they'll call you up and reprimand you. Some of those girls are real mean." Orwell lay in the future, but Big Sister was already at work. It sounded sinister. But then, Anna had not been asked to join, so perhaps, for her, those grapes were sour.

I overcame my doubts and took the plunge. So evenly did the balance waver between two of the sororities that I am ashamed to say I tossed a quarter for it; the coin led me to the eclectic frat whose sisters went out for Activities. At about six o'clock that evening I walked to the house, which commanded a superb view over one of the deep ravines that bit into the hill above Cayuga's waters. There was a crisp, clean smell of woods, of rocks, of fresh air. Below, the long blue lake snaked among tree-clad cliffs and promentories; its depths, people said, had never been plumbed; it was dangerous because of sudden, violent storms, and full of Indian legend.

Even the ravine could be dangerous. It was spanned by a narrow foot-bridge from which several suicides had jumped, and there had been at least one mishap; a student, naked save for a jock-strap and carrying a bowl of goldfish, had plunged to his death. He had been undergoing an ordeal during hazing, that system designed to test the nerve of the initiates much as, in

Africa, circumcision ordeals try the courage of the young before they are accepted into the tribe. At Cornell no one had actually been circumcised but they had been beaten, mildly tortured and scared out of their wits by ingenious tricks and devices. After the foot-bridge tragedy, the authorities had forbidden the more brutal forms of hazing, but it continued on a milder level; you might, for example, be commanded to swallow live goldfish taken from a bowl and thrust into your mouth, only to find, on swallowing them, that they have been transformed by sleight of hand into slices of carrot. I was greatly relieved to learn that hazing was not practised among coeds.

On arriving, together with two other pledges, at the sorority house, the door was flung open and a mob of howling dervishes burst forth, waving their arms, screaming, yelling and capering wildly around the small patch of lawn. Was the house burning, had it been taken over by raving lunatics, had some cataclysmic national disaster occurred? Flailing arms enveloped us, we were pressed to bosom after bosom until I literally gasped for breath. We were made to dance, to hug, to laugh in ecstacies of pleasure. I was not at all good at this, and knew my response to be sadly inadequate. I had looked on the sorority too much in the light of a club, too little in that of a spiritual sisterhood. No wonder Americans regarded the British as a cold, standoffish, frigid lot, barely human. We were. I did my best but it was not enough. The pleasure and excitement of my new sisters was genuine.

Pledging was more restrained. Candles were lighted, we stood in a circle with bowed heads, we recited prayers and the president pinned a small emblem to each initiate's dress. Our novitiate lasted for six months. During that period we could withdraw if we wished, or be discarded by the sisterhood. Such events were rare. Meanwhile we got to know our new sisters and could use the chapter house at any time, dropping in for a meal, or to spend the night, in an atmosphere more intimate and cosy than that of a large dormitory. While the ecstacies of pledging day were not repeated, it was the duty of our sisters to make us feel welcome, and this they conscientiously performed with smiles, greetings and an occasional warm hug as they sped about their business; for there was no idling at Cornell.

12

There could not be. There was study, so much more crammed and unrelenting than at Reading; there were Activities, so numerous and taxing; on top of this, the majority of students were working their way through. This meant that instead of sitting down to a reasonable meal between studies or Activities, they were serving it to others at cafeteria, frat house or dormitory; before their first lecture began at eight o'clock, they had put in a couple of hours delivering milk or newspapers, stoking furnaces or sweeping paths; that evening home-work had been combined with baby sitting, and that they had spent in bakery and laundry, behind the soda-fountain in the drugstore, wiping windshields at filling stations, setting type for the *Daily Sun*, or serving in the co-op, time that their lazier counterparts in England might have frittered away in punt or café, library or common room, or in cycling about country lanes. The standard rate of pay was fifty cents an hour for men and thirty-five cents for girls.

Most students had their fees paid by their State, but must provide for their own board and lodging. Whether or no their parents could afford to foot this bill—and probably most could not—it was a point of honour to pay it by their own efforts. Almost everyone found paid jobs in the long summer vacation, but this was not enough. Every frat house and dormitory, male and female, gave free places to a few students in return for free labour. All the domestic work and the upkeep of the campus was thus provided for; in this respect the university was like a huge medieval monastery. In those days of prohibition it even brewed its own wine from raisins and concoctions in laboratories.

The energy of my fellow-students never ceased to amaze me. Soon I was caught up as if in a whirlpool, hurled hither and thither, from lecture to seminar, library to lab, drill-hall to playing field, meeting to party, picnic to football game. No time to stand and stare indeed, and no place for the solitary. Relaxations were communal. I had not been a fortnight on the campus before I experienced my first picnic. This took place at night and was what would now be called a single-sex event: all girls, and several hundred girls at that. Dressed, to a coed, in breeches, sweaters and windcheaters, we proceeded in a fleet of buses to the shores of Lake Cayuga, where we debussed and

were issued with hot dogs, doughnuts, apples and coffee, all
ready waiting for us in a boat-house. We carried our hot dogs
to an enormous bonfire cackling on an open space nearby and
toasted them, and very good they were; then, gathered in a
circle round the bonfire, we sang college songs punctuated by
hillbilly tunes which were then in fashion, and folk-songs like
"Riding Down from Bangor", and ballads that evoked legends of
the opening of the West, the great days of the rail-roads and
Indian wars and 'fortyniners, legends that seemed very close in
time in these surviving woods and beside these Indian waters.
After about an hour of song we re-embussed and drove home.
We all enjoyed it, but why we had to wear breeches remained a
puzzle.

My next picnic also took place at night and once again we
wore breeches, this time to better purpose, and there were
fewer of us. A party of four or five set forth just before sunset
in a puddle-hopper, as that tattered kind of open vehicle was
called, stopping in the town on the way to buy food and petrol.
A boy of fifteen or sixteen filled our tank. "Going for a picnic?"
he inquired, "Mind if I come too?" He squeezed himself in and
off we rattled to a nearby state park, where everything was
beautifully arranged: a wide parking place under the trees, a
stone fireplace with a grill for cooking, piles of logs stacked
beside it, sawn and split, with heaps of kindling. All we had to
do was to set a match to it and toast our hamburgers.

A creek ran past the picnic ground, embracing a narrow
stream. We followed it up a little way. There was something
curiously dead about it—no wild life, no fish, very few birds. A
century ago, less probably, it would have been busy with
beavers working in their lodges on every stream and rill. This
was all great beaver country. The wealth of the rich Empire
State was built upon their pelts, exported in bateau-loads down
the river and then to Europe, to be transferred from the backs
of the trapped creatures to the backs and heads of prosperous
male humans, and exchanged for more useful commodities like
rum and gunpowder. In due course the beavers were extermin-
ated and silence now enfolds the creeks.

Although it was late October the woods, warmed through by
Indian summer, were almost stifling, the ground dry, and so

we decided to sleep out. We had a rug or two in the puddle-hopper and this was all we needed; there was no wind and no touch of frost. The filling station boy went down to the highway to thumb a ride home. It was silent in the woods, no birds called, nothing rustled the fallen leaves. Sounds of locomotives, a dog's bark, a faint chime of a clock stirred the air across a tip of the lake which lay there invisibly in the dark, pointing a narrow finger up to Canada.

Those bygone beavers had shared this country with Indians; Cayuga was the name of one of the Six Nations of the Iroquois league who, like the beavers, are no more. They had fought as British allies against the French, and the British in return had guarded their territory against land-hungry American settlers who pressed up these valleys from the seaboard towards the fat and fertile western forests and plains. Then came war, and the Six Nations, honouring their treaties with the British king, fought for the loyalists against the rebels in their customary fashion, wiping out entire settlements with tomahawk and fire and not sparing women and children. It was not surprising that the American victors sent an expeditionary force into western New York to quell the Indians once and for all. They did it thoroughly. Muskets and fire destroyed this rich land; villages were razed, fields of corn and orchards burnt and felled, live-stock obliterated. This western country had been the granary of the Six Nations and they never recovered.

At the head of Lake Cayuga was a village, and of this no trace survives, The drums of Cayuga can sometimes be heard on still days or nights. I thought this was a legend only, but I heard them once myself, the following summer, on a burning, sultry day in July. The university had disbanded, a sleepy peace possessed the hill. I was sitting under some rocks, with a long view up the lake, about seven o'clock one evening, and I heard a long low mutter from the north, towards Canada. Thunder on its way, I thought; and yet the sky was clear. The sound came again, closer, this time not so much a mutter as a throb: low, steady, like a pulse-beat, like a drum. Then silence, and then for a third time the sound came, even closer, even more like the steady throb of a drum.

I asked one of the professors for the scientific explanation.

"There's been plenty of research," he said, "but it's gotten nowhere. There are plenty of theories—echoes of distant thunder, wind currents funnelled through the hills. Nothing proven. The legend is, there's an Indian village buried down under the lake. The drums beat a requiem for their people, whom the white men drove away."

That night, so silent were the woods you could have heard the ghostliest footfall of a feathered brave, or a splash of furred beaver. Though ghosts were all about us I heard nothing, and slept soundly on the dry, clean-smelling leaves.

Chapter Sixteen

THREE Englishmen, all post-graduates, shared an apartment in the town. "The son of a lord, the son of a professor and the son of a coal miner," I was told. "Isn't it peculiar that they'd agree to live together? Since they're English, I mean." Although they knew that, in theory, the feudal system had weakened its grip in Britain since the Middle Ages, few Americans had managed to rid their minds of images of serfs and vassals, probably in smocks, pulling forelocks or dropping curtseys to barons who swept by in chariots, scattering largesse if in a good humour, otherwise flinging the vassals into dungeons, or at the least into the stocks.

The son of the lord was lanky, studious and reserved—he came from Edinburgh. The son of the professor was almost everything that most Americans imagined Englishmen, other than lords and vassals, to be, except that he did not wear a monocle: a beefy, pipe-smoking rowing blue who kept himself aloof, professed to hate women and to be a connoisseur of beer. He disapproved of co-education. One coed described him to me as "that guy who talks as if he had no teeth in his head," which was how a Cambridge accent sounded. The son of the miner, James Brown, was a geordie; he was thirty years old and had supported himself since the age of fourteen on scholarships, fellowships and bursaries. He intended to continue in this career. "It's a sheltered life," he said, "with regular meals."

It was he who took me to my first campus dance. Every weekend at least a dozen of these events were held in the various frat houses, and by the clubs and associations which abounded. They could be either hops or formals; for the formals, as the name implied, you wore evening dress, and so you sometimes did at hops; it was hard to distinguish one from the other, especially as the evening wore on, the punch-bowl was continually replenished and hip-flasks passed from hand to hand.

This was at the height of the prohibition era, which had spawned a new folk-lore of speakeasies and hijackers, moonshine and rum-runners, hooch and gorillas. We knew all about it from movies, newspapers and writers like Dashiel Hammett, and such names as Al Capone and Legs Diamond, George Remus and Bugs Moran, were household words. What I had not realized was that a lot of Americans took prohibition very seriously and believed in it; many Cornell students did not drink at all, even cider, and some of the frats were dry. Others, on the other hand, were not.

There was nothing dry about this first hop I attended, or about subsequent ones either. A large bowl of fruit punch stood on a table in the entrance hall and each young man, as he came in, emptied the contents of his flask—or one of his flasks—into it. The flask might contain bootleg whisky, bathtub gin, fortified wine or almost anything; chemistry students could generally get hold of absolute alcohol, used for preserving specimens, as undiluted as its name suggests. The punch then became spiked, and was ladled into tumblers with an outsized soup-spoon. People knocked back most of the tumbler's contents in a single swallow. I tried to do so, but could get no further than about three gulps; it was like swallowing liquid fire, followed by the sensation of being hit on the head by a shovel. My admiration for Americans who could take this in their stride and get degrees and earn their keep into the bargain, swelled like an inflated balloon.

Balloons, indeed, seemed shortly to be all about me, their colours indescribably bright, their antics prodigious, and accompanied by fireworks; my feet felt like thistledown. At least they did continue to support me; others were less fortunate. Before long people were going down on all sides. When I saw a girl trying to rise from a window recess, wobble a few paces and collapse in a heap on the floor, I thought she had been taken ill. A couple of boys picked her up and carried her out. "She's just overshot the mark a little," my partner said unconcernedly. A little later, screams of uncontrolled hysteria broke out; another girl was trying to tear off her dress and more or less succeeding, until forcibly removed by another set of swains.

You did not need a chucker-out at these hops, but you did need a good supply of carriers-out. The liquor seemed to affect the girls more than the boys, though you were apt to come across apparently dead male bodies hunched up in the car-park, overcome while fetching fresh supplies from automobiles, or propped against walls or steps. "The liquor hit them," people said. Hit was the word. There was always a chance you might go blind. Quite a lot of people did, during the thirteen years that the Eighteenth Amendment remained in force. I never heard of an authentic case on the campus during my single year there, but after this initial experience tended to keep off the spiked punch just in case, and because I did not enjoy the sensation of being bashed on the head by a shovel. The contents of hip-flasks were safer, and no college boy was properly equipped without his flask, just as every frat house had its official bootlegger. People discussed their bootleggers rather as they might their doctors; a good, dependable man was needed, one you could rely on even if you paid a little more. There was an Italian barber just off the campus who supplied any kind of liquor at cut prices, but with him you took a bit of a risk.

The faculty also had their regular bootleggers, and would help their students if need be. "Do me a favour, honey," Billie said one day as I was setting out for a lecture. "Bob's coming up this week-end and I have to meet him at the depot; will you stop by at Professor Bally's at six o'clock and pick up a bottle?" Now that I was pledged, Natural Intercourse had been restored between Billie and myself and we were good friends.

I was naturally glad to do her errand; but it was not as easy as it sounded. To begin with, the campus was enormous. Huge buildings, each devoted to some branch of learning, were interspersed among wide lawns and separated by gulches and canyons; a network of roads criss-crossed the domain and you might have to traverse several miles to get from one lecture to another, or to the football stadium which held tens of thousands, or to the gothic and cathedral-sized Sage Chapel, or to Willard Straight hall with its theatre, its restaurants and cafeterias, its club-rooms and terraces and lounges, its guest-rooms for visiting alumnae and relations; or to the co-op almost as crowded and diversified as Selfridge's; or to the pig-styes of Animal Husbandry in one direction, the multi-storeyed dormitories in another, the various frat houses and professorial residences in a third. The drill hall of the R.O.T.C. was of a size to accommodate six full-sized indoor tennis courts, and track meets—athletic contests—were held inside it. Most students had puddle-hoppers to get about in, but I did not, and no one had bicycles as had been the custom at Reading, whose entire university could almost have been accommodated in one of the blocks.

So it was no simple matter first to locate Professor Bally's; there was a book in which you looked people up; this gave a code number, and you found the building on a map. Then you had to reach the building, and on this occasion the campus was deep in snow. The roads were kept clear, but if you tried a short cut you found yourself crunching through a foot and more of crisp, icy snow that gave way with a satisfying kind of squeak. It was like a walk through icing sugar. All the buildings looked white and noble, the air was clean and pure, the lake frozen, and in the afternoon covered with skaters swerving and swooping like swallows over a pond; the air was cold and made your lungs tingle, it was all stimulating, exciting and beautiful; it was good to be alive.

By six o'clock it was dark, and lights shone across the snow; one thought of good king Wenceslas, carol singers and birds with feathers ruffled, of holly and brandy-snaps. "Sure, sure," Professor Bally said, emerging from his warm lighted nest carrying a package wrapped in newspaper. "Tell Billie it's five bucks and it's okay." I trudged off into the snow. The campus was pretty well deserted by now. As I passed the chemistry labs, a figure white as the snow around us leapt from a patch of bushes and stood in my path, waving its arms. It was a completely naked man whose skin glistened with oil. I dropped the bottle and an armful of books and gaped, too startled to be frightened, and wondering if I had sampled the hooch without remembering what I had done.

The naked man waved his arms, gave a sort of grin and pranced off across the campus in leaps and bounds, like a sportive deer. I recovered the bottle and books and resumed my long walk with anxiety, but the man did not reappear. Nor had he been an hallucination; others, I learnt, had seen him, always at night, leaping out of bushes at single or at pairs of girls. All he did was prance and wave his arms, he never laid hands on anyone, let alone raped her, and so, while disconcerting, he was harmless. He was also cunning, and though the police laid traps for him, baiting them with girls, he did not fall into one for a long time; nor did he contract pneumonia, in spite of being naked in the snow with the temperature down below zero. When, eventually, he was apprehended, he proved to be the son of a judge and a third-year student in good standing, who led a normal, blameless life in every other way; unsustained, too, by a hip-flask, which could not be carried by a naked man.

Those who could afford it went to the other extreme and wore raccoon coats, in which they looked like shaggy black-and-white bears; pockets were stuffed with hip-flasks, especially at football games in the fall. James Brown took me to my first football game. The movies had introduced me to the general idea, but black-and-white pictures gave no inkling of the colour involved, and colour played a big part; nor was I prepared for the scale. And Cornell games were a pale shadow of the really big stuff, such as the Yale-Harvard game, for which New Yorkers paid twenty or thirty dollars to secure a good seat, or events held in the famous Rose Bowl in California, whose university had the largest campus in the world, and the most ebullient football team whose supporters released gigantic flocks of white pigeons, each trailing a crimson ribbon to animate the brilliant sky.

We had no pigeons at Cornell but we had cheer-leaders—everyone had them. After we had assembled in the stadium, thirty thousand of us I believe, and bought our chewing-gum and bags of popcorn (how good it was!) from white-clad student vendors in pork-pie hats, there was a hush of expectancy. Then, from beneath the stands, the cheer-leaders burst forth like so many toreadors, clad in tight white trousers and short crimson jackets and carrying megaphones. Each had a section of the stadium for his territory. At first, each young man crouched close to the ground, palms flat, like a frog; a mutter like the distant sound of breakers began to issue from the stands. The cheer-leaders then dashed along the ground in a half-crouching position, like squirrels; the cheering slowly gathered force. Suddenly they sprang high into the air like so many Nijinskys, every finger outstretched; the cheering burst forth in a mighty roar. Each one behaved as if his body was a baton in the hands of some frenzied maestro of the spirit world. They were pulling the sound out of our throats, playing on us like supremely skilled orchestral conductors. The sounds that actually emerged were frightening in their strength and volume but banal in form.

Cornell I yell—yell—yell—Cornell!
C—O—R—N—E—L—L
C—O—R—N—E—L—L
Cornell, Cornell I yell, yell, yell—
Cornell, Cornell, Cornell.

After each crescendo these incredibly acrobatic young men executed a series of cartwheels, handsprings and somersaults while we regained our breath; then we, and they, were off again, the air shaking as if with thunder; the cheering must have been audible miles away. Although the success of the Big Red Team could not have been a matter of life or death to either of us, James and I yelled our heads off with the rest. We could not help it, we were swept along. Goodness knows what those red-and-white clad young men could not have made us do; tear each other to bits I daresay; but they stuck to the routine, and we to our part as rooters cheering on the Big Red Team to victory.

In the British sense of the word it was not a team: eleven young men, that is, on each side, to fight it out to the end. It was a squad. Thirty or forty players sat on benches, wholly encased in armour that gave them the look afterwards accorded to spacemen, except that their protective clothing was leather rather than plastic; perhaps they were more like hoplites, with cumbrous leather breast plates and greaves and enormous helmets, each of which must have weighed at least ten pounds. Mostly they entered the fray for fairly short periods at a time and then withdrew, to be replaced by others according to the swaying fortunes of the battle. For it *was* a battle, not a game.

The generals were the coaches on each side, and the contest was more of a battle of wits between these doughty individuals than a trial of speed and strength between the young men. The coach's job was to assess correctly the qualities of each member of his squad, and to throw into the battle, as it proceeded, whichever players best met the needs of the moment, and withdraw those whose skills were not being fully deployed—as well, of course, as the flagging and the wounded. So armoured figures were constantly pelting on to the field, trotting back from it or, more rarely, being carried off on stretchers. The fray itself, which took place on a so-called gridiron (the field being marked into ten-yard strips) was by British standards very static; every yard gained was fought every inch of the way, and pauses for tactical discussion between groups of players who whispered to each other through their ear-flaps with their arms around each other's shoulders, were frequent and could take place, apparently, at any time.

These details may not be quite accurate as, despite a good deal of coaching myself, I found the game's complexities hard to master. I did not wonder that the coach's salary was about double that paid to the President. The coach was obviously worth more. No academic contest would have attracted thirty thousand paying spectators who yelled their heads off, their throats hoarse and their flasks dry, on a cold, raw afternoon. Besides, the contributions forked out by alumni helped to finance nearly all the universities; victories on the gridiron warmed alumni hearts and opened alumni pocket-books, whereas if the Alma Mater kept on getting beaten, her alumni grew disgusted, and cut off supplies. To sign up a really good coach was therefore more important than to sign up a good President, and anyway they were scarcer. The names of famous ones like Knute Rockne of Notre Dame were household words, and their autographs fetched as much as the most glamorous of film-stars.

Any lad who had distinguished himself in high school football was certain of a place in college, quite without regard to his brains—though not at Cornell, which was proud of belonging to the Ivy League and therefore in the same class as Harvard, Princeton and Yale, though at a lower level partly because it was coed. Nevertheless, boys who had their letter—a large white C sewed to their maroon vests—could count on a certain leniency among their professors, even on a little flexibility when it came to marking papers and awarding grades. A real moron would not get by, but the eye of the needle might be widened a trifle to let through a border-line case.

The grandest spectacle occurred at half-time when two bands paraded, one attached to each team. Their uniforms were magnificent and their precision every bit as fine as that of the Brigade of Guards. Each band was led by a drum-major whose twirlings and jugglings with his baton could have been surpassed by no professional. Many colleges had gone over to drum-majorettes, who, in kilts and highland bonnets, were as neat, sightly and deft of movement as tropical fish; but Cornell, although coed from its foundation, was always trying to pretend that it was not, because of keeping up with Harvard and Princeton; so it did not have drum-majorettes. The all-male bands with their fifes and drums, bassoons and cornets, paraded and cross-paraded and formed the initials of their teams. Overhead appeared two aircraft, painted in Cornell colours and trailing banners; their pilots cut out the engines, swooped low, and crooned in amplified voices: "I'm high, high, high up in the clouds, smoking Old Gold cigarettes."

When a game took place away, we rooters repaired to the Drill Hall, where a gridgraph was installed. A gridgraph was a huge green board set up against the wall and marked out to scale like a football field. I was introduced to this not by James, but by a young lecturer in pomology called Milton, whom I had met at one of the Bristow Adams's Monday evenings. We paid a dollar each and took our seats on the stand. Out came a full-scale band, every bit as resplendent as the number one band which had gone to Philadelphia with the team. Then came red-and-white cheer-leaders, turning cartwheels and doing hand-springs with every bit as much verve as those we had seen in the stadium; I suppose there was a panel from whom were picked the best dozen or so. On the gridgraph were the names of all the members of the Big Red Team, and a light sprang up beside any of them who had contact with the ball. Another light dodged about dementedly, representing the ball itself; by these means we could follow every twist and turn of the game. When a goal was in sight, or a disaster loomed, we were stirred to frenzied cheering by the tireless acrobatics of the cheer-leaders with their megaphones. Hip-flasks came out, even though there was less cold to keep at bay; but there was sure to be either a victory to celebrate in the finish, or a defeat to drown.

"People take it all so seriously," I said to Milton as we made our way to a cafeteria when the last cheers were done. "They seem to *mind* so much who wins."

"Sure, they mind who wins. Don't you?" Milton was clearly puzzled by my comment, as a theologian might be puzzled by a comment that the members of a priesthood seemed to mind whether or no there was a God. "Everyone likes to see his Alma Mater win."

"Yes, but it's all so *organized*."

"You think we should muddle through, like the British? Trouble is, the British muddle, but they don't always get through."

Since the existence of Milton's nation was a proof of this, and anyway Anglo-American arguments were to be shunned, I dropped the subject, but could not forget it; the regimentation of American life was possibly the quality, more than any other, that made America a foreign land. I missed that quality in British life Rupert Brooke had summed up in his words: "Unkempt about the hedges blows An English unofficial rose." Yet the reverse of this, the tulips blooming as they were told, Germanic discipline, was not here either. An American tulip would bloom as it damned well pleased, and to put up a *verboten* sign would be an open invitation for its immediate and violent demolition. Americans were not casual, unpunctual, individualist, sloppy and prone to improvise as we were, content with the second-best and ill-designed, taking pride in failure and in gallant last stands, and in sheer crass stupidity like the Charge of the Light Brigade; but nor were they content to be ordered about as apparently the Germans were. They were neither one thing nor the other; they were something else. But what? They took delight in organizing things, they were communal in spirit, like bees; they were fantastically energetic, they cared terribly about winning, and they went in for theories much more than we did. That was about as far as I could get.

Matters like this were sometimes touched upon at Bristow Adams's Monday evenings, to which Milton always came. I think he was lonely, though I could not be sure; there was something elusive and impersonal about Milton to my mind, though possibly not to his countrymens'. He was not at all shy, but fond of expounding, and had excellent manners, handing round coffee and asking how many lumps of sugar and moving chairs and shifting ash-trays to anticipate the needs of others. Milton was tall, spare and very slightly stooping, with long arms and crew-cut hair that started high up on his forehead, and rimless spectacles; he looked, and was, diffident and earnest, and born to inquire into things. For him the world did not exist to relax in or exploit or take for granted, but first of all to try to systematize, and then to improve.

For Milton everything must have a reason somewhere, if you knew how to find it, and everything could be made better, and one day *would* be made better, than it was now. His faith in the perfectibility of man was unshakeable, but he had reservations about God, although his father was an itinerant Wesleyan preacher from Ohio, and Milton had moved from school to school and never settled anywhere for long, or owned possessions. He had carried his school books around in a battered old case held together with binder twine and done his homework in barns and corner drug-stores and the vestries of chapels, and in the holidays sold Fuller brushes on commission to pay for his clothes, which had always been shabby. (They were neat now, always clean and pressed although of cheap material, and he wore a bow tie with polka dots.) Despite these handicaps he got himself to college, worked his way through to secure his B.Sc., and was then awarded State grants for post-graduate study that enabled him to specialize and become, as he now was, a lecturer in pomology.

Pomologists, I learnt, studied apples. There is a lot to the study of apples; Milton was busy with research into the inheritance of immunity to certain bacterial diseases. On the one hand this might lead to a practical way of growing apples more efficiently, on the other it reached right down into the mystery of life, into its chemistry and mechanisms of inheritance; so in a sense it spanned everything from the secrets of the universe to the bank balance of people like Anna's father. "The world in a grain of sand," Milton quoted. "Heaven in a wildflower, and infinity in the palm of your hand. That's right, too; that's how it goes. The sublime mixed in with the ridiculous. And New

York is our third largest producer of apples." That was typical of Milton: Blake and the Bureau of Statistics intertwined.

"Why do Americans always want to beat each other, to excel?"

"Because we are dominated by our women," Bristow Adams answered. "We can't boss them around as European men do, so we take it out on each other. We're a society of frustrated, therefore quarrelling, males."

Bristow did not appear dominated by anyone, certainly not by his wife who was a gentle, kind, domesticated woman devoted to her family and good at making pies. They had a tame chipmunk in the woodshed and fed birds all winter; Mrs. Adams made her own clothes, had a store-cupboard full of preserves and pickles, and painted flowers on china. Bristow was a New Englander but, in practising the journalism he now preached, had travelled all over the United States, spent years in Washington and acquired that profound scepticism about politicians universal among political correspondents. Now, to augment his salary—professors were then atrociously underpaid—he ran a page of household hints, recipes and advice on matrimonial problems in one of the national weeklies under the name of Marianne Mackintosh. I came to love them both dearly, and Bristow's old mother-in-law who had so romantically travelled in a covered wagon on the Oregon Trail, and heard the war-hoops of Indian braves, and seen the last great bison herds.

Milton did not agree with Bristow in ascribing to sexual frustration the American desire to excel. "It's because we've had to master our continent, and still have this to do. Think of the Pilgrim Fathers: each man with an axe, a tinder-horn and faith in God, and that was all. With that equipment he stepped ashore to face three thousand miles of forest, rock, prairie and mountain, peopled by hostile Indians, and he had to subdue it. And he did. Or the strong ones did, the weak perished. That pattern is still being repeated by the immigrant who comes to the city with nothing but his two hands and his ambition. He makes it or he goes under. Rugged individualism has been cheapened by the politicians but it's the thread that runs through all of our history."

But it was not rugged individualism, I suggested, that seemed to a European, at least to this European, to characterize American life so much as a contrary inclination to cluster: to join groups, clubs, societies, chapters, teams and act together; to become an Elk or Buffalo or Rotarian or Mason or Daughter of the American Revolution or sister of the Ancient Order of the Nile; or, at the least, Cincinatti treasurer for the class of '21, or chairman of the Epsilon alumnae chapter of Alpha Sigma, or president of the Glee club, or fixtures secretary of the mycologists' circle, or convenor of the study group on the philosophy of Swami Babu Bai. Americans out on their own, not in a group, felt naked, unprotected, insecure. If the campus was a microcosm, they were the world's greatest joiners of committees. There was a committee for everything you could think of and for many things I would have defied anyone to imagine.

"That's part of the pattern," Milton agreed. "If you have enough committees, then everyone on the campus has a chance to be a big shot in a small way. Everyone can pat his chest and say: I'm president of the society for the introduction of the Ohio grading scale in potato riddles; and he'll rate a mention in his home-town newspaper. Forming committees is the oldest of American customs. I don't doubt the Pilgrim Fathers formed one just as soon as they stepped ashore. Even the Revolution was run by a bunch of committees, the Committees of Correspondence that kept the revolutionary spirit alive."

Was this, I asked, an efficient way to run a war? "You couldn't have a less efficient way. Committees quarrel, argue, dither and delay. They get themselves tied up in red tape, they can't make up their minds, they let opportunities go by, they water down decisions to a point where they don't make sense. But we won the Revolution and King George didn't. They're part of the American Way."

"Talking, then—is that the American Way?"

"Yes, talking. Letting off a lot of hot air, allowing all the screwballs to shoot their mouths and wasting a lot of valuable time. But getting our minds made up in the end. And then acting, every one of us, acting together. And going on till we get what we want—kind of obstinate. That's the real American Way."

Milton believed in it with all his heart, but not aggressively

13

as some did, those who were unsure of themselves. Bristow showed his students how to put it all to good use. It was true that, as Milton had said, by reason of the number of committees, groups, societies, chapters or teams open to him and requiring office-bearers, almost every student could achieve some honour, which his home-town newspaper would be happy to report. Soon I was dispatching to the *Ticonderoga Times* or *Pine Bluffs Chronicle* or *Spencer City Courier-Gazette* brief home-town-boy-makes-good items which they invariably printed, though without payment; as a rule they sent a copy, I cut out the story and pasted it into an exercise book, and it counted as a credit in Bristow's course. If you sent a photograph which was printed, you scored double.

So every day I scanned the *Sun* for news of campus appointments, tracked down the person mentioned and hurried off to interview him, or her, before others got the story—thereby becoming competitive too. It bit you, the get-on bug, you could not avoid its mandibles. And this was not a bad training in the basis of the journalistic craft. It taught you to keep your eyes open for news, or anything that could be turned into news, and it taught you that the essence of news was, and is, what people do. And you never knew what they might do next on the campus. Once, hearing strange noises around midnight, I looked out of my window to see a man tearing off all his clothes, ripping them to pieces, prancing on those he could not destroy and kicking up a tremendous shindy. This was in winter, with a near-zero temperature. Ought I to call the police? Several other windows opened briefly, a firm female voice said "Hush." No one paid further attention, and eventually the man went away. "That was just Franny's boy-friend," I was told next morning. "He thinks he's not had enough attention lately, I guess. He's quite ardent."

By contrast, I was startled, on a hot midsummer afternoon, to see a number of red devils skipping down an avenue, whisking long tails and carrying pitchforks. No one else seemed to find the sight unusual. Proceeding, I came upon a portly, heavy-jowled Turk wearing a tarboosh and a kind of toga, talking to an even paunchier pirate with large black moustachios and a cutlass tucked into a red sash round a protruding middle.

Large black numerals, stitched to their attire, labelled them respectively '89 and '93.

After the red devils, who I now saw were labelled '08, came a squad dressed in white ducks with scarlet cummerbunds, shirts to which spine-pads were attached, dark glasses and solar topees; they pounded by singing "The Old Grey Mare" with great spirit. And from beneath topee and tarboosh, devil's cap and pirate's tricorn, peered almost identical faces: square-jawed, puffy, sallow, flat, lined, with small eyes and often rimless glasses: the unmistakeable face of the middle-aged, generally Mid-Western, business man.

This was Reunion Week when, from every State, alumni converged upon their Alma Mater for a week's immersion in a Lethe that washed away conjugal obligations, community demands, the burdens that for the other fifty-one weeks of the year weighed down the stooping shoulders of all these respectable benedicts, model fathers, home-town boosters, go-getting business men, sound Rotarians. They called back yesterday across the years, uncovering memories of the slim young men who'd made the baseball squad, gloried and drank deep with fraternity brothers, and dated the prettiest coed in the class of '15. It all went by classes—the year in which you graduated; each class had its fancy dress, its officers of course, its chosen songs, its programme. A silver cup was awarded to the class showing the highest proportion of attendance at the celebration. I do not know which class won this in '28, but it should have been the class of '69, represented by a single ancient, revered like a visiting god, the sole survivor of his class which was the first ever to graduate from Cornell.

For a week, these middle-aged gentlemen—and ladies too, though not in such numbers—galloped about the campus chanting college anthems, in their fancy dress; attended dinners, sing-songs, get-togethers and formal receptions; got drunk together, prayed together, went on picnics, cheered at baseball games; told dirty stories, slapped each other on the back. They recalled the heroes of their day: crew captains, stars of the track, class presidents, the Big Red Team; and did not appear to find anything incongruous in the sight of the treasurer of the Cedar Falls Community Chest Fund, or the branch manager of the

A. and P. in Medicine Hat, dressed as highwaymen or Robin Hood's archers or Roman centurions and singing The Old Grey Mare or, in more solemn vein, the dirge-like chant:

> High above Cayuga's waters
>   With its waves of blue,
> Stands our noble Alma Mater,
>   Glorious to view . . .
>
> Lift the chorus, speed it onwards,
>   Loud her praises tell:
> Hail to thee, our Alma Mater—
>   Hail, all hail, Cornell!

From the university's point of view, they hailed it to good purpose; they brought their cheque-books and there was not one who did not leave behind in the Alumni Office his mite towards the magnification of Cornell: now and again a pretty sizeable mite, even a new building on which his name would be graven over a Corinthian portico or under a Palladian architrave. It was genuine, this moist-eyed loyalty to class and college, to comrades in arms when the world had been an oyster and the sword bright. And then midnight struck, and the devils and explorers, highwaymen and Sherwood Foresters turned back into real estate operators, vacuum cleaner salesmen and corporation lawyers. Back with them to Cedar Rapids, back to Pine Bluff, leaving the campus to today's crop of slim young men loping by in maroon vests with a proud C, or rattling past in puddle-hoppers from frat house carousels, headed for a date with the prettiest coed of the class of '29. And behind these my contemporaries, across the summer lawns, flickered mocking shadows of the thick-hipped, sallow men they would become with heavy jowls and paunches and anxious eyes peering through octagonal lenses at the slim young men of the class of '58 loping by . . . Little wonder that The Old Grey Mare sounded less like a drinking-song than a dirge.

> . . . ain't what she used to be,
> Ain't what she used to be, ain't what she used to be;
> The old grey mare, she ain't what she used to be . . .

They did not believe it, of course. She had become a better horse.

Chapter Seventeen

FROM early October until the end of June we pursued our studies interrupted only by a few days off at Thanksgiving in November, at Christmas, and between the two semesters into which the academic year was divided. This break came in February and was known as Junior Week, a time for lovers among students as among birds.

You might have expected that, with so strenuous a fall behind them and an even more strenuous spring, if such were possible, ahead, this would have been a time for the students to rest and relax. Perhaps those who went home did unwind, but in Ithaca a sort of campus saturnalia took place. Each fraternity gave a house-party. Weeks ahead, preparations began; floors were polished, curtains cleaned, empty bottles trucked away, food laid in. Bootleggers' trucks drove up to house after house disgorging cases labelled Canned Peaches or Best Preserves. The richer frats ordered dance bands from New York. Florists came to make costly arrangements, and then arrived chaperons engaged for the week: possibly a married couple, or a respectable middle-aged woman, probably someone's aunt. The chaperon's function was to remain calm in all circumstances, to know when to look the other way, to stay sober and to keep up appearances.

Then came the guests, mostly girls from women's colleges like Vassar, Smith, Wellesley and Bryn Mawr. Some might be coeds, but in general coeds enjoyed, or endured, a lower social rating than girls from women's colleges. Bids to house-parties in Junior Week were much sought-after, especially, of course, those from members of the smarter frats. Dances took place every evening and no one got to bed until daylight, if then. During the night there was a good deal of going if not actually to bed, at least to a parked automobile.

Did any coed remain a virgin after four years of college? Who knows? People were always trying to find out—national magazines, churches, researchers into sociology, earlier Kinseys;

questionnaires marked "Confidential" arrived continually. One, I remember, posed the question: "Where did you fall?" The answers, duly correlated, digested, tabulated and abstracted, revealed what everyone knew: number one, the back seats of automobiles. Number two was the family living room and ten a.m. oddly enough, the most popular hour. Then came the porch, presumably in rocking chairs. The surprise, to me, was that canoes came fifth. It would be difficult, I thought, to surrender one's virginity without literally rocking the boat, but then nearly all Americans learnt to swim in high school, most of them were good at it and life-saving was a widely taught skill.

No one can ever know the truth about these matters because no one will tell the truth, even—or perhaps especially—in questionnaires. The Walter Mitty fantasy enters deeply in. But my fellow coeds discussed it all with a great deal more candour than I had encountered in England. It did not seem, to them, an especially private affair.

The principal deterrent, insofar as there was one, appeared to be less the fear of pregnancy which in Britain, in those pre-pill and pre-loop days, held back the more cautious, so much as fear of disease. Whether this was more rife in the United States than in Britain, or merely more openly recognized, I do not know, but would guess the latter. Notices were displayed in many places about the dangers and symptoms of syphilis and gonorrhoea, and of addresses to apply to for treatment or a check-over. There had been nothing of the kind at Reading. Here at Cornell, those who fell, whether in an automobile or a canoe, were more apt to seek absolution from a doctor than from a priest.

Treatment was by no means either quick or easy; this was in the pre-antibiotic age. I heard a sorority sister remark that her home-town doctor had been warning her about the perils of campus life. "I like to sleep with one of the boys sometimes when I feel inclined," she said, "but he was most discouraging. He quite put me off." A girl who had transferred from a mid-Western college related how a fellow coed had been found in bed with a man in her chapter-house; her sisters had immediately summoned a doctor, not to take steps against pregnancy but to check for disease. Then they had evicted her; morality was stricter in the mid-West than in the East. Even here, whatever might occur in Junior Week at house-parties, in normal times boys were expected to behave with decorum in sorority houses, and love-making to be relegated to auto-mobiles.

This did not apply to love-making between girls, which could take place indoors. Considering the pronounced heterosexuality of campus life, it was unexpected to find lesbianism quite popular as well. There was a pair of lovers in Prudence Risley and sometimes, if you went into their room, you would find them snugly curled up together on the bed in each other's arms; they did not spring apart or make any pretences; it was just an accepted arrangement. Both were pleasant, friendly girls, and both had boy-friends with whom they went out regularly and whose fraternity pins they wore; one subsequently married her boy, and when by chance I heard of her some twenty years later, she had become the mother of seven. My sorority house had a sleeping-porch with beds in tiers, and there was always a spare one available for any sister who wished to stay the night. The house also had a pair of lovers, and sometimes you could hear the springs creaking as they bounced about overhead, but no one paid attention, or regarded them as pariahs.

At first, this came as a surprise. Lesbianism was something I had heard about but never, as it were, seen in action; there had been no lesbians at Reading so far as I knew. But perhaps I had simply not known, owing to our British reticence; the place, I now realized, may have been full of secret or suppressed lesbians. Although recognizing how much more sensible it was not to keep these matters hidden, the subject of half hints and innuen-does, it was some time before I was able to get over feelings of embarrassment at their overt expression. I suppose that I had hitherto assumed homosexuals, whether male or female, to be different from the rest of us, owing to some aberration of the hormones, and that they fell in love only with members of their own sex. That they could have love affairs with people of both sexes concurrently came as a surprise. Betty on my corridor really loved the boy she duly married; did he know, I wondered, about her room-mate Olga, and if so did he mind? And again, at the sorority house, Jean wore the pin of Theo, a serious-minded young engineering student with horn-rimmed spectacles and hair *en brosse*; did he know about Muriel and did *he* mind? Sometimes another boy joined up with them and all four went together to the movies or on jaunts in Theo's car, which would develop into necking parties at the least, possibly more. And possibly not; the right true end of love, I suspected, was by no means always reached. If that were so, perhaps the lesbianism arose because it met desires aroused but not satisfied. Certainly it was more convenient, and safer both from pregnancy and from disease.

I must not exaggerate its prevalence; such happy pairs as Betty and Muriel, Jean and Olga, were exceptions. It was the fact that they *were* happy, or appeared so to be, not hunted or shunned, that impressed me. The British were always saying how barbarous Americans were about sex, and it took me some time to realize that all they were doing was to revert to an outlook that had probably prevailed in the original Ithaca. In classical Greece, no one had ever supposed that you must love either a member of your own sex, or a member of the other, but not both at once; they would have thought the notion ludicrous. It was for the unrequited love of Phaon, the god-like boatman, that Sappho was supposed to have leapt from a rock in Lesbos, not for the love of any of her circle of maidens who may well have been students under instruction in the arts of poetry rather than of love. British standards, I came to realize, might not be the only ones, and they might not even be right.

The British were always sublimely certain that their ideas enjoyed both prerogatives. As a colonial, I could understand the irritation this aroused among lesser breeds, and resolved to avoid, if I could, giving offence. This meant conforming with American customs, rather than damning any that differed from our own as examples of crude and vulgar ignorance. So, if I went on a blind date and necking was expected, necking there would be; I would not hang back like some timid prude, earning a bad name for all British girls. At first, the prospect filled me with misgivings. If it had been Turner, now—but it was not; I was not promiscuous by nature and I, too, was nervous about pregnancy and disease. Such words of high praise for an escort

as: "Boy, is he a heavy necker!" or: "My, is he a fast worker!"
had an ominous ring.

It was not as bad as I expected. Most of the blind dates
turned out to be soppy rather than impetuous; they kissed, of
course, and fondled, but while resorting to well-tried devices to
arouse desire, were content to leave it unsatisfied, and to lie
for long periods more or less immobile, curled up like hiber-
nating bears. The full rights of love were not, as a rule, accorded
unless you wore a boy's fraternity pin, or demanded unless this
had been given; the pin was the pledge. If you finished with a
boy, you were supposed to return his pin; but my friend Billie
had a mania for collecting them, and kept eight or ten in a
drawer. She had promised Bob never to go out without his pin,
which acted as a warning-off symbol to other men, the mark of
someone else's territory. "When I go out with another boy,"
she explained, "I wear his pin on my teddy, so I don't break
my word." A teddy was the silk slip worn by some coeds; others
wore no underclothes at all. One acquaintance peeled off her
dress to reveal herself naked but for a strip of adhesive tape
bridging the buttocks. "It improves my silhouette," she said.
Out of doors, everyone wore hats.

Milton continued to remain an enigma. He seemed to seek
my company; he took me to the movies sometimes, and afterwards to a restaurant in the town where you sat in cubicles in
semi-darkness and consumed food that looked appetizing,
smelled good but always tasted the same; he escorted me sometimes to football games, track meets and plays at Willard
Straight. Sometimes he took me for a run in his puddle-hopper
out into the woods and creeks and hills that lay all around. He
could not take me to his home because he had not got one; his
father continued in his nomadic task of carrying the Word of
God to folk pretty familiar with it already, in small mid-
Western towns; his mother was dead, and a married sister lived
in Minnesota. But he did not park his puddle-hopper by the
roadside and get down to business, and when we said goodnight
he would give me a chaste little peck on the cheek, no more, and
sometimes not even that. I had never repulsed him; he just had
not tried. Was it my fault? Was he simply very shy, and was it my
duty to overcome this and to arouse his ardour? Did I lack some

clue to the correct behaviour in a situation of this kind? I felt
sure that Billie, say, or Jean or Anna, would handle it differently.

Perhaps he had selected me for his companion because he did
not want to be handled by someone like Billie, Jean or Anna. At
any rate this rather pale relationship suited us both, and I did
nothing to upset it. Milton could be an informative, if not a
sparkling, conversationalist, with an interest in history as well
as in pomology. He believed in the approach of the millennium,
if in slow stages, and would sometimes, on Monday evenings at
the Bristow Adams's, read aloud from the epic poem *John
Brown's Body* by Stephen Vincent Benet, and the stirring
affirmations of belief and patriotism by Carl Sandburg. Most
girls would have found him boring and perhaps that was why,
in his mild way, he had fastened on to me; I was willing to put
up with a little boredom as the price of protection from the
feeling that I ought to keep up with the Billies and Annas of the
campus in parked automobiles; and anyway I did not find him
so boring as they would have done, because the history was new
to me, and being the son of an itinerant preacher seemed to me
extraordinary, whereas most of my fellow coeds would have
found it commonplace.

Things might have gone along like this indefinitely had it not
been for a picnic which took place in early spring. Winters at
Ithaca were hard and beautiful, with snow lying deep in the
gorges, and clothing the campus in a white unbroken sheet,
innocent of footmarks; with ice thick on the lake, air clean and
sparkling, and at night, under a full moon in a star-pricked sky,
a fairyland ethereal splendour that struck at the heart. Spring
was late and sudden, and at first raw; there was grey slush
everywhere, water racing down the gorges, dripping trees and
buffeting winds. Then, suddenly, it was almost summer; the
slush had gone, the gales ceased, birds fluted, the sun warmed
the nape of your neck. You could feel growth everywhere,
before you could see it. Animals lowed from barns where they
had spent the whole winter, warm and dry but bored. Farmers
mended fences, greased machinery, dressed seed corn. Buds
thickened and swelled. By northern European standards, everything was telescoped; one forgot that New York City has the
same latitude as Madrid.

All this led to picnics, among other things. You still had to wrap up warm and take rugs, but the air was clean and fresh as mountain springs, and you drew it into your lungs voluptuously, and felt light-headed and alive, and the heavy cares of study, of trying to understand and to remember, above all to remember, fell away like the winter fur of beasts. You went into a mental moult.

This picnic originated at Bristow Adams's and about a dozen people went. There had, of course, to be liquor, which the men arranged between them to supply. As a scientist, Milton was detailed to bring a flagon of wine from the chemistry laboratories. This was a red, fiery spirit that stung as it went down and burnt the stomach when it arrived, and resulted in a singing head and weak knees and immoderate laughter; but it was reliable, in that it had never made anyone blind. Milton seldom drank himself, and then only beer, but he did not mind bringing the wine.

We drove along a road that twisted through woods above the narrow lake, blue as ever above its buried drums, until we parked the cars and walked a little way up a creek, carrying our rugs and cushions and equipment, and found a sheltered place under some rocks. A spring trickled forth, ferns sprouted from the rocks, birds were chirping, but the woods themselves were silent and unpeopled; we were alone. Milton looked quite sportive in a new bow tie with green dots, and a pair of yellow laced track shoes; he plunged into the woods with a companion who was interested in spiders, and they returned in high spirits with several captives in match-boxes, while Milton had found a kind of shrub that excited him, because it was suspected of acting as host to a moth whose grubs parasatized a wasp that in turn acted as a predator of a pest of apple trees.

This, he felt, might be an important discovery. So he was in a mood to celebrate, and did so by washing down hamburgers toasted over a fire with the chemical wine. He did not drink a lot, but you did not need a lot to get results. The flagon went round several times and after a while none of us, sprawling on our rugs, could have got to our feet had we wanted to; the potion had an extraordinary effect upon the knees. It also made one's head buzz and spin. I lay back to ease a heavy weight that had settled on my eyeballs, yet feeling as if I was floating on air. People were singing, I was singing too, Milton was singing and waving something in the air—the branch of his precious shrub, I believe. Then, much to my surprise, he cast it aside and enfolded me in his arms. This struck me as so funny I began to giggle, and once started could not stop. A fear that this might hurt Milton's feelings was the last thought I remember, as stars began to pivot and explode behind my eyes.

When I came to I had a splitting headache and felt very sick; the same trouble had overtaken my companions, who lay sprawled upon the rugs in various attitudes of inertia, or were staggering unsteadily from behind trees. "Boy, was that stuff wild," said one, shaking his head like a dog coming out of a stream. "Kicked like a horse," another agreed. "Is everyone okay?" No one was dead or blind. Milton had disappeared. What had happened? Had anything happened? Impossible to say. We got up unsteadily; at least our knees worked. We drank from the stream and felt better.

In a remarkably short time, we were recovering; splitting headaches began to abate. Milton reappeared, rumpled and silent and without his rimless glasses. "Have you lost them?" I inquired. "Lost what?" "Your glasses." He fumbled in his pocket. "I guess I must have." There was a search and the glasses were found, unbroken. "I'm glad of that," I remarked, for something to say. Milton nodded. He seemed to have lost the power of speech, avoided my eyes and in the car sat silently beside me, fingering his temples now and then. The whole thing was most unnerving. Milton was suffering: I was not quite sure why, or what I should say, if anything, to console him. For my part, I did not know whether I had cause for anxiety, and if so what I should do about it; even if I ought to see a doctor, I did not know the name of one to consult. All I was sure of was that in future I would shun all forms of hooch, however reliable.

A few days later he rang up and made a date at one of the cafés. He was still ill at ease, and several conversational trails petered out before he remarked as he stirred his coffee, his eyes averted from mine:

"I guess I owe you an apology."

"I don't see why."

Milton frowned at the cup, stirred more vigorously, cleared his throat with a hoicking sound like the preliminary to a spit. "For behaviour more appropriate to a beast than a man."

"People are unfair to beasts when they say that. There's nothing wrong with beasts' behaviour really."

"It's true they don't surrender to intoxicating liquor. Whereas I've read that the only race of man that didn't discover the technique of fermentation were the Eskimos."

"I suppose blubber won't ferment."

Milton nodded approvingly, perking up a little. "Quite correct. There is no sugar in blubber."

"I suppose not."

Milton cleared his throat again. "Anyways, I promise you it won't occur again."

The question was, had it occurred at all? Milton evidently thought so, but he might not know either. The uncertainty was disturbing. In a roundabout way I consulted Billie, who set my mind if not quite at rest, at least more nearly so, by repeating in different words the observations about drink and lechery made by the porter in Scene iii, Act 2, of *Macbeth*. "They can't do it when they pass out, honey," she said. Hoping that Milton might take the reference I remarked: "Well, drink is a great equivocator, it's been said."

"It is the greatest enemy to the progress of mankind," Milton pronounced.

Chapter Eighteen

ONE of the strangest men I met at Ithaca was Chester, formerly of the Royal Navy. He was about thirty when he came to Cornell to take a short course, one year, designed for practical farmers. He turned up one evening at Risley hall and asked the first girl he encountered to take me a card. She handled it gingerly, as if it might sting; we were not used to cards. "He looks kind of cute," she said, "like he was an uncle." If he was an uncle, he was not mine.

"You're English, aren't you?" he inquired. I said that I was mainly Scots in origin. "It's all the same here," he said. "I thought I'd like to hear an English voice again. Shall we sit down and talk?" He did most of the talking, in a pleasant, rather clipped voice. He had golden hair sprucely brushed, a freckled sunburnt skin, a shapely chin and little tufts of reddish hair inside his ears, and wore a black homberg hat tilted at a jaunty angle that doubled back his right ear. His eyes were greyish blue and pale, woodsmoke colour, and looked right through you sometimes, when his mind wandered off on its own.

If he was English, he was not buttoned up in English reserve; rather he was forthcoming like an American, and quickly told me his story. When the war ended he had left the Navy and roamed about the world doing many things: he had been a consul in Holland, a tourists' guide in Italy, a boatman in Kashmir, dogsbody on a wheat farm in Western Australia. Then he became a supervisor of female cashiers at the Wembley amusement park. It was during this period that he fell in love with an American girl he met one Sunday afternoon in the British Museum. It was a fateful meeting. Margaret responded with friendship but not with passion, and Chester laid himself and all that he was and had at her feet. He followed her across the Atlantic to press his suit and the trail led to a small college near Athens, in western New York, whose students were instructed in Greek drama, as well as in music, ballet and other branches of the arts. This was another link between them, for

Chester was an ardent Hellenist who had taught himself Greek in order to read the great dramatists in the original, and try his hand at their translation.

This college, or school, had been founded by Margaret's parents, who had also been English, and had also left their native land impulsively. In his youth, Chester related, Margaret's father had written a play and sent it to Sir Beerbohm Tree, who had returned it with a rejection slip. Several years later, the disappointed dramatist had seen a play produced by Tree almost identical in plot with his own composition. In high dudgeon, and after having failed to get any satisfaction from Tree, Margaret's father had shaken the dust of England from his shoes and emigrated, never to return. He had married a dancer, the school had taken root and thrived, and their daughter had grown up to become one of the instructors.

Despite Chester's devotion, Margaret could not requite his love. "I guess she never will," Chester said.

"Then aren't you wasting your time?"

"No, indeed. If she were to say tomorrow that she'd marry me I don't know what I'd do—run away, probably. Marriage kills romance. True love is murdered by propinquity, by routine, domestic friction. After the first row at the breakfast table, love lies bleeding."

"But you can't go on all your life as you are?"

"Why not?" Chester said. "Dante loved Beatrice all his life and never married her. After a while I'm quite sure he didn't *want* to marry her; she was an ideal, a star in heaven; she inspired his verse. If she had borne his children he would have been writing grocery lists instead of poetry. No. I shall go on loving Margaret from afar." He quoted *La Belle Dame Sans Merci*, but although in a sense loitering, he did not look pale or bewitched. Chester looked robust, worked on an apple farm when he was not at college, and had taken out his first citizenship papers; after five years, he would renounce King George and become a full-blown American.

"Suppose Margaret marries someone else?"

"So did Beatrice; Dante's love never faltered. She remained perfection in his eyes. So will Margaret in mine."

Our acquaintance did not exactly ripen but continued on a

casual, friendly level; we met for a cup of coffee now and then, and occasionally encountered each other in the Animal Husbandry block, where Chester was taking a course in hogs and I was concerned with starch equivalents and bovine metabolism. One week-end we boarded a train called the Black Diamond that ran to Buffalo, visited Niagara Falls, dined in Canada, drank a glass of indifferent but non-bootleg port, and watched the falls lit up by million-candle power searchlights that turned the tossing spray in turns red, green, white and purple. It was impressive but somehow insulted the great falls, which could impress without being tarted up by human devices. As it was, they were nearly overlaid by factories with tall chimneys and the paraphernalia of turbines and dynamos. The music of tumbling water was punctuated by the shriek of locomotives and the rumble of trains. Up in the trees, out-sized hen-coops labelled Honeymoon Huts swayed and trembled in a cold north wind. The headlamps of automobiles formed an arc over the river.

"It's changed a lot," Chester remarked, "since 1812."

It must have, I agreed; but why 1812? Thereby I displayed a sorry ignorance of North American history shared, I am afraid, by many of my fellow-countrymen. If 1812 means anything to most of us, historically speaking, it means Napoleon's retreat from Moscow. In 1812 the North Americans, whether in Canada or in the newly united States, were too busy fighting a desperate and bloody war of survival to care two cents about what was going on in Russia. Niagara Falls I had heard of mainly as a place that honeymooners flocked to; I had not even known that it lay at the centre of a great battle-field; and that the battles fought there had decided the future of Canada.

Chester enlightened me; one of his forebears, he said, I think a great-grandfather, had taken part in some of these battles. On the Canadian side a bluff rose above the river which he said was Queenstown Height where Isaac Brock had fallen. I had never heard of Isaac Brock, but gathered he was a kind of minor Wolfe, and a national hero. The Americans had been resolved, Chester said, to destroy once and for all the forces of King George on the soil of North America, and they also wished to liquidate the surviving Indians, who went about scalping settlers and were egged on, in their belief, by the British. An American army burnt and utterly destroyed York, which rose later from its ashes to become Toronto. Finally a great battle was fought on Queenstown Height, full of hand-to-hand combats and so bloody that eventually Chester's great-grandfather, a young captain, was the senior surviving officer and took command. "He got a bayonet wound in the shoulder and another in the leg," Chester recounted, "but he carried on. Both sides fought themselves to a standstill and eventually the Americans left the British in possession. All this took place so close to the falls my great-grandfather wrote in his diary he could feel the spray on his face. Soon after, the war ended—and we kept Canada." We felt proud of our victory and of Chester's heroic ancestor, whose health we drank in a second glass of indifferent port. "He married a squaw," Chester concluded. "Or at least if he didn't marry her, he should have. He left her behind and settled in Bodmin." I wondered how much Chester had made up, and how much was in the history books. Certainly he made Niagara Falls much more interesting than a mere collection of factories and Honeymoon Huts encircling coloured spray.

This was in winter, when the spray had frozen like crystal on twigs and branches all around, and the New York country-side was white and empty, the fruit trees all bare. In the spring he took me on another jaunt, this time by car and farther afield, to the New York–Vermont border. It was a long drive north through Syracuse and Utica in the Mohawk valley, then over a spur of the Adirondack mountains to the little town of Ticonderoga on the southern tip of Lake Champlain.

Ticonderoga was a plain little town much like any other "in the sticks" where life revolved around the corner drug-store with its counter at which you sat to consume your ice-cream soda, maple sundae or coke, and where you paid your dime or nickel for a packet of roasted popcorn, some chewing gum or a couple of luridly illustrated pulps. We stayed the night with acquaintances of Chester's, an elderly couple more or less retired—from what, I could not discover: business of some kind. They had a bit of land and kept a few poultry and pigs, made their own butter and preserves and cheeses, manipulated an old cider-press in a shed, and took in summer visitors.

14

Theirs was a curiously old-fashioned, self-contained existence, the antithesis of anything I had thought of as American. New York City might have been in another continent, and was more alien to them than to me; if they visited a city it would be Albany, the State capital. Movie-house and radio brought the outside world to them and yet they remained enfolded in their woods and mountains, well content with uneventful lives: going regularly to church and twice a week to the movies, visiting each other's wooden houses, each with its porch, each much alike but individual, for bridge and teas at which anything but tea was served, buying brushes and encyclopedias from travelling salesmen and shopping more ambitiously through mail-order catalogues. Everyone knew everyone else and all about him; there were feuds and rivalries but no class distinctions; people believed in God and in the Ten Commandments; sinners and the young tended to leave town for wider opportunities. Ticonderoga was indeed a peaceful spot, but this had not always been so: it came into history books and had been French until the British took it and established a garrison there to hold at bay hostile Indians. The redcoats in their turn had been displaced in the first year of the Revolution by the storybook hero Ethan Allen and his eighty-three Green Mountain Boys, who had marched through the forests from Vermont to surprise the British commander in his nightshirt.

Lake Champlain runs northwards into Canada and its eastern shore lies in Vermont. Chester drove me a little way along the Montreal highway, past the old fortress at Crown Point. We stopped at an inn where a hiker's trail took off, and followed a winding path a mile or two into the woods. The day was crisp and clear, the sky a tender blue, the sunshine still mild, not summer-hot; there was a smell of growth and renewal in the air. Trees were bare still, but their buds swollen and a purplish tinge lay over all, with traces of dark red. Some years later, I drove along this highway in the fall and the fierceness, the intensity and the sheer magnificence of the gold and scarlet hit you like a blow; it was as if every hill and valley was ablaze, or showered with gold, and the long thin lake, curled like a dragon, reflected it all. For about three weeks this glory lasts, then the leaves fade and everything is russet. Now, in spring, it was grey and silver, and dark green where hemlocks stood bunched together on the Green Mountains. These woods could have changed little since Indians hunted here, and the bugles of the soldiers thinly floated up the valleys from Crown Point. We returned a different way and, just off the highway, came upon a small, ramshackle house that advertised refreshments, so we stopped to ask for a cup of tea. Chester said that in New England you could sometimes get proper tea, even though most of the genuine Yankees had left years ago for fatter regions, leaving the rocks and barren hillsides to Irish, Polish and Italian immigrants.

This house had none of the trim, well-tended look of most New England dwellings. The steps were half rotted, rockers and straight-backed chairs on the porch were worn and broken, bits of old newspaper lay about and everything had a melancholy, neglected air. An old man appeared, white-haired and stooping, his hands crabbed and veined but with a keen, frosty eye; he spoke with a high, whining Yankee twang and spoke as little as possible. A Vermonter all right. In silence he put down a battered tin tray with a pot of tea on it and made no response to comments on the weather. When he brought the bill we made one more effort. Below us the clear, still blue lake reflected a tracery of oaks and maples. There was a little inlet, with a narrow sandy beach. A dinghy with a white sail went by close inshore.

Were storms bad, I asked, on Lake Champlain? No answer. Did vessels ever sink? He jerked a thumb.

"Wreck down there." What sort of wreck? "The Congress galley." What was she? The old Vermonter, who never looked at either Chester or myself directly, gave a snort of contempt. I pressed on. Who owned her? He emitted a brief cackle.

"Congress, I guess."

"Who sailed her, then?"

"Sailors. Some of 'em."

I floundered on. "What happened to her?"

"Burnt."

"Burnt by whom?"

"The traitor."

I gave it up, and Chester laughed and said that now I'd met

a real New Englander. The old man cackled to himself and went off to get change. When he came back he did not leave immediately, but stood for a few moments looking down into the inlet. He had a dark, weather-beaten complexion and cocked his head to one side. Then, to our surprise, he lowered himself into one of the rockers and started to talk in his high-pitched, vigorous voice. Evidently he had decided to make a clean breast of the shipwreck.

How much of what he said was true and how much legend, I do not know; Chester said that part of it was in the history books, about the battle between Sir Guy Carleton's ships and those commanded by Benedict Arnold, but not of course the part about the witch; though this, too, he might have got from some book of legends. The crabbed Vermonter had a pawky sense of humour that would find satisfaction in taking anyone for a ride. Afterwards I wrote down the story as he told it, so vividly I could see it all happening down in the inlet as if I had been there.

The original cabin, on the site where this crumbling house now stood, had been built by Prentiss Teller. Who was he, I asked? A Yorker from up the Mohawk somewhere who hunted with the Indians and traded in furs. All this was Indian country then and no settler was safe, but Prentiss was the Indians' friend and so they let him alone. Also, his mother was a witch. She lived with her son and the Indians let her alone too. Her familiar took the form of a chipmunk, an extra large one with yellowish fur, who followed her everywhere and used to perch on her shoulder, chattering, and run up and down her arms.

One day Prentiss came back from Albany with news that something big was happening down at Skenesborough, on the upper Hudson. A dockyard had been fixed up there and they were building ships—not ordinary bateaux but schooners, galleys, sloops. General Arnold was doing it, he said—next to Washington the finest general in the Continental army, idol of Connecticut and the New York militia. Folk were still talking of his great march to the St. Lawrence across the uncharted wilds of Maine, six hundred miles through swamps, forests and mountains, at the head of a thousand militiamen carrying bateaux and provisions, until the provisions gave out and they boiled their elk-hide breeches to yield a little broth; and then their desperate attack on the stronghold of Quebec. Now Arnold was back, striving with all the zeal of his fiery nature to build and equip a navy that would halt the invasion planned by the British down the Hudson Valley from Montreal. And at the north end of the lake, at St. John's, the British had fitted out a three-masted brig, two schooners and twenty gunboats, and were making ready to sail.

Prentiss Teller went north to join his Indian friends and see this fleet sail. The Indians were British allies and so Teller was on the British side. His mother watched Arnold's Congress fleet sail north past her cabin from Crown Point on a fine September morning: sixteen sail bristling with cannon, flags fluttering bravely from mast-heads. They were sailing out to meet a fleet superior in numbers, in fire-power and in skill. The Congress fleet was manned mostly by militiamen, the ragtag of New York and Connecticut, who'd never sailed a vessel in their lives before.

Prentiss Teller returned a few days later to say that Arnold's fleet was at Valcour Island, about halfway up the lake. Next morning, while he and his mother were at breakfast, they heard a low booming roll down the calm surface of the water from the north.

"They'll be blowing Arnold's fleet to smithereens," Prentiss said with satisfaction. "It will soon be over." But the booming went on all day, like distant thunder, and got heavier in the afternoon. The sun was dipping behind the wooded brow of the Adirondacks before it ceased. Prentiss was uneasy; the fight had gone on for so long, like a man kicking after he'd been hanged.

He went north again next morning and came back with strange news. Arnold had held the British off all day, he told his mother. He'd lost his ship, but got aboard another. The British had stood off in the evening, thinking to finish him in daylight. At dawn they saw only empty waters. Somehow or other, almost a miracle, he and his surviving vessels had slipped away in the night.

Soon after sunrise, Prentiss and his mother saw several ships sail by close together, battered as thrown-out saucepans—their sails in tatters, splintered decks, busted rigging. But they moved, and a mist hid them from their pursuers who were close behind: guns opened fire as the mist cleared. At first, fountains leapt up where shots fell short, but the British were gaining on the two Congress galleys. Soon a broadside smashed into one of them and made her reel; another volley followed, her masts were shot away and her sides holed; she was done for. The flag at her mast-head fluttered slowly down.

The other galley fought on. Grapeshot whistled through her rigging, round shot slammed into her sides. Prentiss could see the figures on her deck scurrying to and fro. One in particular caught his eye: here, there and everywhere, now siting a gun, now directing repair of rigging, now helping to carry off a wounded man. This embattled galley bore slowly down the lake like a deer bayed by a pack. Six or seven ships were after her, raking her with broadsides. She was holed a dozen times and it seemed impossible that she should still be afloat. Prentiss realized Arnold's intention: he meant to turn her up the inlet, run her ashore and make a dash for it, and never strike his flag.

The galley ran in and grounded. Over her side leapt a number of men armed with muskets. That short, active figure Prentiss had picked out during the action was still aboard, running hither and thither with a lighted torch in his hand. Soon flames began to leap and cackle and smoke to billow from the wreck. The commander was the last to leave; he leapt from the bowsprit, his coat blackened with powder and stained with blood. His flag still flew from the mast-head of the Congress galley, now alight from stem to stern.

One of the crew collapsed in jumping from the vessel. Two men ran back to carry him up the slope. Prentiss, deeply moved by all that he had seen, now emerged and led them to his cabin, and helped to lay the wounded man on his mother's bed.

"We'll tend him," Prentiss kept saying. "We'll tend him till he's mended. A man who fights as he did, he deserves it."

Then Arnold came in. He knew that the British would send their Indians after his escaping crew. Prentiss knew this too. "You'll never out-distance them," he said. "Your men are exhausted. If you take the trail to Crown Point, you're done for."

Arnold laughed, and merely asked Prentiss's mother for a glass of water.

"The Indians know you'll make for Crown Point," Prentiss persisted. "They'll set an ambush for certain. I can show you another way through the woods. If you'll trust yourself to me, I'll bring you safely to Crown Point."

Arnold took the mug of water that Prentiss's mother had poured for him. But he never drank it. The chipmunk leapt from the old woman's shoulder and landed on his wrist, knocking the mug out of his fingers. The creature had been chattering away in a state of disturbance ever since Arnold had entered the cabin. With a swift movement, Arnold grasped the chipmunk as it leapt for safety and in an instant it lay on the table with a broken neck.

Prentiss Teller guided Arnold and his men back to Crown Point by a roundabout way, avoiding the ambush that the Indians, as expected, laid for them. The Indians returned empty-handed to Sir Guy Carleton.

When he reached this point the old man paused; he seemed to have reached the end of the story.

"She turned turtle and sank," he added, "the Congress galley. That's where she lies, what was left of her—down in the creek."

"And the old woman—the witch."

The old man cleared his throat. "All talk," he said. "Nothing better." The injured man left in her cabin had turned up a few weeks later at Crown Point, his wounds healed. No one had expected him to live, still less to walk back under his own steam, a whole man. The old woman, he reported, had applied poultices and given him draughts made from roots and herbs from the woods. No doubt she knew a lot of Indian secrets, and maybe other things as well.

This soldier had a queer story about a glove that Arnold had dropped somewhere near the cabin. The old woman had picked it up and she talked to it, the soldier said, as if it had been an animal, and put it on her shoulder; and sometimes she laughed at it in a way that scared him. No one paid attention to his story. They thought he was light in the head from loss of blood, and sent him home.

"But nothing ever did go right with Arnold after that," the

old Vermonter concluded. "He licked Burgoyne, but never got the credit. He didn't get his rights from Congress either— someone spited him there. So something went wrong inside of him. A devil got into him, I reckon. Must of been that, for Arnold was a fine general and a brave man. Wasn't a better rebel in America, till a devil got into his soul."

"So the old woman was a witch after all."

"She was a Dutch," the old man said. "Came from Pennsylvania. I reckon Arnold never ought to of killed that chipmunk. If he'd let it alone, he'd 'a died a hero. But he lived a traitor, and a devil had got into his soul."

We left the old man silent in his rocker on the dilapidated porch in the backwoods: so silent, I wondered whether he had spoken at all, or whether I had imagined the story. The waters of the inlet placidly reflected boughs and blue sky. How much of the tale was history? "The battle part of course," Chester said, "off Valcour island, and Arnold's escape. I don't know about Prentiss Teller and the witch. He may have read it somewhere or it may be local legend. And in a way he was right about Benedict Arnold. Congress slighted Arnold, he was passed over for promotion, he married a girl half his age and got into debt. So he fell for British gold. If the old woman really hexed him, she did a good job."

Americans come to England in search of history but their own land is soaked in it, and it is all heroic—battles, sieges, burnings, sackings—Gettysburg and Bull Run, Valley Forge and Saratoga, Custer's Last Stand, Remember the Alamo and Remember the Maine. The Battle Hymn of the Republic would stir the most lethargic, and dull would he be of soul who could remain indifferent, despite their almost endless repetition, to those ringing words spoken first at Gettysburg: "Fourscore and seven years ago our fathers brought forth on this continent a new nation, conceived in liberty, and dedicated to the proposition that all men are created equal . . ."

This landscape is permeated by the heroic, or at any rate by the desperate, violent and brave; here men were scalped, women eviscerated, cities burnt, homes swept away by floods, in later years citizens mown down by Sicilian gangsters. In Baton Rouge you are shown the spot where Huey Long fell to an assassin's bullet on the floor of the State legislature, just as Romans were no doubt shown where Caesar fell in the Forum. Americans share this with the Greeks and Romans, this prevalence of heroes whose godlike qualities lighten human clay; these are common folk in homespun sometimes touched by the fire of Apollo. By contrast, most of our English heroes seem more of a separate caste bred for the job like race-horses: kings from castles, not farmers' boys. They are also farther away in time. Only a hundred and fifty years had gone by since Arnold leapt from the burning Congress galley; Chester's great-grandfather fought on Queenstown Height. A century and a half is a long time, but not as long as the time that separates us from King Arthur and from Charlemagne, from Alfred the Great and from Richard Coeur de Lion. In England you learn history as something that happened once and is over, petering out into details of parliamentary reform and the rise of trade unions, and the death of an imperial dream; in North America, it still seems to be going on.

It was going on with a surprising vigour and immediacy in the minds of some of my fellow students. One of my sorority sisters remarked with flashing eyes: "We Americans will always hate the British; we shall never forget 1776." She was studying to become a school-teacher, and it was a safe bet that on the wall of her schoolroom would hang a picture of a young militiaman departing from the farm kitchen, musket in hand, for the wars. His old mother touches his shoulder with a gesture half of pleading, half of benediction; a small brother trots proudly at his side; in the background an ageing father comforts a sobbing young wife. This is "The Spirit of '76" and it used to hang in almost every school and in innumerable homes from coast to coast.

I found it strange that so forward-looking a people, so rich and powerful, should continue to harbour a grudge against a nation they had defeated a century and a half ago and now eclipsed; especially as more than half our nation, and nearly half theirs, even at the time, had thought the quarrel foolish or misguided. I laid this problem before Milton, who asked: ·

"What do you in England call the war?"

"The War of Independence, I think."

"It wasn't a war of independence at all, to start with, though it turned into that later. It was what we call it, the Revolutionary War. It was a revolution against the folk people always do revolt against, the big shots, the high and mighty who control the government. Most of these weren't British, they were Americans and they stayed loyal to King George. Half the population of New York State were loyalists. They lost out and got kicked out, or fled to Canada. That left the revolutionaries in control—the haters."

"According to you they hated each other, rather than us."

"They hated you too because the upper class was British in tradition, loyalty and outlook. The British were tied up with property, landlords, paying debts, judges and magistrates—all the things that went overboard when the Revolution succeeded. The revolutionaries seized the loyalists' property and that made them hate their former rulers worse than ever—you always hate the folk you've wronged. Americans hate the British primarily because of class, not because of tyranny, though of course the two go hand in hand."

But now Americans, I protested, had classes of their own, and privilege and rich and poor and high and mighty families, so why continue to hold it against us? Didn't they realize times had changed in Britain too? That redcoats, King George, oligarchical rule had vanished? If they thought our set-up was the same as in 1776, then they believed in fairy tales.

"Sure," Milton agreed. "All Americans believe in fairy tales. The log cabin to the White House. There's gold in them thar' hills. You can make your fortune out in Hollywood. Make the world safe for democracy. As for England—there was a King George in 1776 and there's one there right now, crown and all, sitting on a great big empire and saying you can't afford to pay your debts. And as for lords, we had plenty of them here before the Revolution and there's plenty around now, coming over with lah-di-dah accents, and they don't seem to have changed. And I don't believe we like them any better than we did in '76."

I only half believed Milton at the time because I thought, as all British people think, that Americans love lords even when they pretend not to, and envy us our Royal Family even though they disapprove of kings. Later, I came to doubt this. It was easy, then, to be led astray by contacts too closely restricted to members of what are now called the upper income groups and of the eastern seaboard—almost the only people, apart from taxi drivers and bellhops, many English visitors used to meet. Beneath this polite crust lies the half-raw, steamy, meaty pie that is America, in which the British flavour has been overlaid by stronger and cruder spices. To such Americans, most English lords and ladies appeared to be cold, sour, undemocratic and up to no good, to be kept at bay by a strong gulp of the spirit of '76, which remained the one true, native vintage.

Chapter Nineteen

THE last thing I ever expected was to see my cousin Kate in New York City. But then, you would be wrong to expect the expected of Kate. She was looking thin and beaky, in a tight-fitting black dress with false pearls festooned around her neck and the fur jacket that had belonged to Aunt Lilli, and heavily impasted make-up. In one respect she was doing the expected; she was lodged in Greenwich Village, in a small, cramped, none too clean-looking hotel, and in a narrow room with hideous wallpaper, full of things strewn about.

I had received a brief and cryptic postcard from Kate giving her New York address, but omitting to say how long she would be staying or why she was there, and my reply went unanswered. Not long before, Mary Curtin, who had befriended me on the voyage, had invited me to stay in Brooklyn; so, between semesters, I travelled through a snow-clad, frozen landscape to the city which looked more magical than ever with its spires a-sparkle in the frosty air, hard as diamonds, a cold wind ripping through its canyons, everyone hurrying and jostling, taxis honking, lights changing, cops with batons, news-stands everywhere, Negro shoe-blacks, Aladdin-cave-like shop windows, automats and flashing advertising signs never still: the feel of urgency, of purpose, of something about to happen quickly electrified the air. After the smallness of Ithaca it bewildered and alarmed, you were a lost minnow in shoal after shoal of minnows, swimming against a current and pounced upon by pike. How could you not become mislaid among these millions of people, in their turn dwarfed by the depot with its marble halls and no trains? Or, at least, silent trains kept out of sight and approached through burrows, not belching smuts and smoke all over everything as in London, under dirt-encrusted domes.

I did not think Kate looked well. "I hope you're being careful about the liquor," I said. In New York City there were 32,000 speakeasies, and you had to know your way about pretty well to distinguish between those whose liquor was reliable, and those whose was not.

"I'm always careful, coz," Kate said, laughing in her quiet, internal way, as if some innuendo loaded every commonplace remark.

"Who are you with?" I inquired. Kate laughed again, wriggling her shoulders and fingering her pearls. "Shamus came over with a wonderful commission to decorate a mansion on Park Avenue in the style of an Etruscan tomb, for one of the Vanderbilts."

"That ought to take some time. Why does one of the Vanderbilts want to live in an Etruscan tomb?"

"I think because one of the Rockefellers lives in the stately pleasure dome of Kubla Khan created by Salvador Dali. But you must ask Shamus."

"Where is Shamus?"

"Oh, he's around," Kate said vaguely. Male possessions were around but somehow they did not speak of Shamus. The room was over-heated and the window tightly shut. Kate produced a medicine bottle and two tooth-mugs. "You're quite safe, I'd be dead if this wasn't." She poured two stiff drinks; mine made me splutter. "Somehow it seems the wrong time of day."

"British as ever!" Kate remarked. "Everything must have a time of day. Cold bath before breakfast, clean your teeth after it and no fun and games till the sun's over the yard-arm or whatever it is."

"How are things at Nathan's Orchard?"

"Much the same, I guess. I can't say I keep very closely in touch. Mignonette had puppies by a lurcher, I think it was a lurcher, and Bergamot bit Honeysuckle so badly Sir Lewis had to be brought down from London to sew her up. Joanna has mumps and has to wear a plate and Aunt Kitty has given her a sealskin coat, and Nellie had a miscarriage—the last everyone thinks, but then everyone's been saying that for years."

"It doesn't seem to have changed."

"It never will. Mummy writes occasionally on pain of death, and smuggles the letters out by Perce to post."

I did not understand this, and Kate looked amused. "I forgot, that was after you left. I've been forbidden to darken the doors and my name can't even be mentioned, my room's locked and daddy's thrown away the key. I've been expunged."

"No one told me." Since I left I had been told very little; there had been a postcard from Gertrude from Chester, where she had been staying for a hunt ball, and a screed on scented lilac paper from Aunt Lilli urging me to get in touch immediately with a relative of hers, on the Russian side, who had established a camp in southern California where the clientèle, dressed in loin-cloths and *saris*, lived on nuts, dates and *maté*, and shed their physical and spiritual impurities under the guidance of a resident *swami*.

"It was the telephone," Kate explained. "They had it put in, you know, at last, because of getting hold of vets, and Perce's half-crowns each way, and then Berry started ringing up and saying: 'I wanna speak to mah baby, mah cute l'ill baby,' in that divinely attractive voice, and daddy kept saying: 'We haven't any babies here' in that clipped way, you know, more and more distinctly; and finally he shouted: 'God damn it, sir, this isn't a maternity home,' and rang off. Berry got it into his head that I'd been kidnapped, so he turned up in a huge Cadillac to look for me—you can imagine the scene, morose and rather moody in a purple suit with his latest saxophonist in tow. He said he'd come to fetch his baby and it took a long time for daddy to realize that he wasn't looking for a maternity home. When daddy grasped the situation there was a terrific flood of biblical words getting on to the sons of Ham, obviously Berry thought that daddy was a dangerous lunatic, which perhaps he is. I collected what I could and left with Berry, who cried most of the way to London, his feelings were so hurt, and I haven't been back to Nathan's Orchard since. I don't suppose I've missed much. You know Jumbo got engaged?"

"*Jumbo*? I thought he couldn't——" An idea struck me. "It isn't Dando, is it?"

"I think her name's Rhona. She breeds dogs and has enormous feet."

"That's the one. I never knew her name was Rhona. She'll make a home for Patch."

"He said that in the ordinary Navy, he couldn't afford to

marry for at least another five years, so he's transferred to the Fleet Air Arm and thinks he may cut it down to three."

Kate seemed more prepared to talk about other peoples' affairs than about her own. "What are you doing in New York?"

"I told you, helping Shamus. I'm a sort of secretary."

"I didn't know you could type."

"I'm not that sort of secretary. Shamus has been a terrific hit. Everyone in New York is after him, half the society women and all the art galleries." This did not seem to be the sort of room, or of hotel for that matter, an idol of New York would be likely to occupy. A tie with nude girls on it hung over a chair together with a crumpled light grey suit with padded shoulders, and several lurid looking pulps lay around. These did not speak of Shamus; home-woven tweeds from Connemara and a copy of *Ulysses* would be more his mark.

"You won't find him under the bed or anything," Kate said crossly. "If you're so anxious to see him you'd better come to the Algonquin at five, I'm meeting him there."

I had to meet Mary Curtin, however, to be taken to a concert, so we made a date for the following evening, my last in the city. Kate turned up not with Shamus but with a man called Julio, plump and swarthy and in need of a shave. He smiled a lot, displaying several gold teeth, and said that he was in the perfume trade; he gazed soppily at Kate, and sometimes laid a podgy hand with a lot of hairs on it over hers, and kept edging close to her at the table so as to play footy-footy and rub knees.

We ended up at a place in Harlem where a new saxophonist was drawing the town, or as much of it as could be crammed into a low, narrow cellar; the air was thick as putty, the din strident, the heat stifling and there was a sickly undertone, or undersmell, from the reefers which a number of patrons were enjoying. Most of the customers were white but there was a sprinkling of coloured girls, and it was these the saxophonist was really sending. First one would jump up, then another, and start to leap and twist and shake as if galvanized by an electric current; they reminded me of a chicken with its head pulled off that continues to hurl itself about and flap its wings. Soon Kate joined in so expertly that the saxophonist played directly at her, improvising passages for her benefit; she jumped and whirled, jerked and writhed, at the bidding of the wailing instrument that seemed to draw the very blood from your veins. I marvelled at, and envied, Kate's ability to shed entirely all her English stiffness and reserve and enjoy the moment with a lack of inhibition more common among the races of the south, and untrammelled by the anxieties her situation must be causing her. When she returned, flushed and shining-eyed, to the table, Julio patted her arm and said plaintively:

"You left me, baby. You went away and left me."

"Just like Shamus," Kate remarked. "Tit for tat."

"That Shamus is a son of a bitch."

"Shamus is the son of a leprechaun," Kate pronounced with dignity. "A long line of leprechauns. They can't be pinned down."

"Pin down his arse! Do you love me, baby?"

"I love everyone. Deep as the ocean, wide as the sky. I love my cousin. You should love my cousin, Julio."

Julio looked at me more or less for the first time, flashing his teeth; it was one of those undressing looks, starting at the top and running down. "Cousins, hey? Maybe I can see a likeness. Kate is the daughter of a duke. Are you the daughter of a duke, baby?"

"I'm afraid not."

"A royal duke," Julio added. "Wasn't married, though. To her mother. Not in church, see? In the attic."

"Married in the attic?"

"Morganatic," Kate corrected, smiling seraphically; the saxophone had begun to wail again, its rhythm to work like yeast in her blood.

"It was kind of cute," Julio continued. "Every anniversary, this duke sent her mother a very precious jewel in a casket delivered by a masked man riding horseback, with a bunch of tuber-roses thrown in. I like that. Here in New York City a masked man riding horseback with a bunch of tuber-roses would be kind of conspicuous, but in Paris I guess it's different."

"Did Kate really tell you she was born in Paris, begotten of a royal duke on the wrong side of the blanket?"

"She might have embroidered just a little."

"She has a talent for embroidery."

Julio edged his chair closer to mine. "Now you, you're born on the right side of the blanket, I'll bet." His knee pressed mine and his gold teeth flashed. I edged away. It was no good trying to talk; the saxophonist was back in his groove and Kate looked like getting back into it with him. The smoke, perhaps the reefers, made my eyes smart and my throat dry. When the saxophonist paused, a floor-show came on: a pair of enormous, very black female all-in wrestlers, who writhed about on the floor like mountains convulsed by earthquakes. It was hard to tell if they were making love or pulling each other apart: both, possibly. No one paid them much attention. The atmosphere thickened, my temples throbbed and ached; it seemed most unlikely that the hooch would be reliable, and I only sipped mine. I did not want to break up the party, if you could call it that, and said that I would find my own way home; but Kate, by then, seemed glad enough to go.

Mary Curtin had left thin sandwiches and a vacuum flask of coffee for me on a table, and brought me breakfast in bed soon after I had consumed them. The orange-juice was ice-cold, the coffee fresh and fragrant; there was thin Wedgwood china, a starched tray-cloth, even a carnation in a little bowl on the tray. Everything in her apartment was just as it should be.

"I hope you had a swell time," she said. "It was nice to meet up with your cousin like that, and see a little of the nightlife of our great city. Of course it's very crude compared to Paris, nothing like Montmartre they tell me. Dangerous, too, with all this dreadful moonshine; but I don't suppose your cousin's beau took you to that kind of place." I said I had avoided moonshine, and enjoyed the orange juice, but did not really want a coddled egg. "It's too bad you have to go back to Ithaca after such a short visit. You should have spent at least a day at the Metropolitan, there's a Renoir exhibition opening next week and we might have heard Toscanini conduct the Philadelphia. But you must come back for a longer visit when you leave school."

I would like nothing better, I said; meanwhile, there was the question of Kate. "I could let you have ten dollars," I had offered, when the taxi had dropped me at the subway. "That's

15

sweet of you coz, but I'm all right—Julio's got plenty." "But Julio might . . ." "Julio might what?" Kate had asked sharply; he was in the taxi, she stood outside in her short fur jacket; it was bitter cold. "Run out." She laughed. "He could pop his gold teeth." She ignored the alternative meaning. "If you're stuck, come to Ithaca. I could find you a bed somewhere." "I'd be frightened of the Indians." "I wish you'd go home," I said. "I haven't got a home to go to, have I?" "Aunt Lilli might send your fare." This time Kate almost doubled up with laughter. "Aunt Lilli would send a pair of handcuffs I should think, if she sent anything." Julio was making impatient noises from the taxi. "So long, coz, and watch your step with all those dashing students." "Don't forget . . ." She had hopped into the taxi and its light had winked down the street; snow was falling as I went into the subway and thought suddenly of Arnold, who had refused to strike his flag.

Junior Week was over when I got back to Ithaca; trucks had collected loads of empty bottles from fraternity houses, girls huddled into fur coats had said their farewells at the depot, bleary-eyed young men with queasy stomachs had swallowed black coffee in the cafeterias, classes were assembling in lecture rooms. There was skating on the lake, track meets in the drill hall, rowing practice on indoor machines, Gilbert and Sullivan in the Willard Straight theatre; there was the library, the labs, prelims and credits, papers and marks; coffee and waffles, cokes and hot dogs.

I heard no more from Kate for three weeks or so, and then she telephoned. She wanted to come to Ithaca. "Is there somewhere I can stay for nothing?" She sounded rather desperate, and I could only hope the sorority would have her for a few nights. "I won't stay long," Kate added. "Just a change of air." "When can you come?" "Well, right away, I'm at the station." There were clicks and voices. "I haven't got another quarter, goodbye."

Kate was thin as a rail, her eyes enormous, she looked bloodless and brittle and very cold: she wore a thin, hopelessly inadequate cloth coat. "What's happened to the fur jacket?" "I got bored with it, and anyway it kept moulting, and Julio gave me a glorious beaver." "What's happened to *that*?" "It got

stolen," Kate said shortly. "I wish you wouldn't ask so many
questions, coz."

The girls at the sorority house could not have been kinder;
they made a great fuss over her and fixed her up with a warm
coat and told her she was very welcome to stay as long as she
liked. The house-mother, Mrs. Dimple, warmed to her at once.
Mrs. Dimple was one of the most self-effacing women I have
ever met, who turned not one blind eye, but two, and deaf ears
as well, to everything; she drifted amiably about, arranged the
flowers, patted out cushions, emptied ash-trays, answered the
telephone and did the marketing; if anyone was sick, she brought
them aspirins. Here, at last, was someone she could really mother.

Kate, to my surprise, took at once to the campus, and went for
walks in the snow. "It's lovely," she said. "Like the downs only
more so. Can I borrow some skates?" I thought her legs would
snap if she skated, they were like those of a bird. She took an
interest in the birds, and saw a cardinal, fabulous in its scarlet
plumage, like a drop of blood against snow and bare trees. "I'd
no idea America was like this," she said. "Why do people live
in the City?" I kept swallowing back questions that were always
on the tip of my tongue; Kate knew this and tormented me by
remaining secretive.

"Where are all the boy-friends?" she demanded. "Can't I
meet some?" I doubted whether they would interest her with
their talk of basket-ball and athletics, games and marks and
frats, and few had any money to spend. There was Chester, but
he was so detached and dreamy; still, he was kind. We met at a
café in the town and I also asked Milton; he was not Kate's cup
of tea either but I thought he would be restful; what she needed
now was to relax. Chester entered with his black homburg
tilted at its usual angle, crumpling one ear, very clean-cut and
British, with a friendly spaniel expression; he looked much more
reliable than he really was. Kate gave him an appraising glance.

"Are you a professor? I'm not used to clever people, so don't
expect intelligent remarks."

"Good lord, I'm no don," Chester responded; but the little
drop of flattery had found an open pore. "Milton is, more or
less," I told her. "At least a budding one. He professes apples."

"Apples," Kate repeated. "They started all our troubles didn't they—apples and curiosity. Milton had better watch out." But she only flicked her eyes over his attentive, indeterminate face and turned back to Chester. "When I was a child I lived in an orchard, a very ancient one with rotting trees covered with moss and spotted toadstools and with hollow middles where all sorts of things nested, owls and lots of woodlice and squirrels, they hid their nuts there and curled up for the winter snug as a bug in a rug, warm and dark and safe. I wish we could curl up for the winter, don't you?"

"That must have been the red squirrel, *sciurus vulgaris*," Milton pointed out. "I believe the North American squirrel, so-called—not a true squirrel of course—is replacing the native species in many parts of the British Isles." "That generally happens to natives," Kate said. "They get replaced. Like your Indians. Have you any Indians here?" "Not right here on the campus," Milton answered, "only East Indians. They're very conscientious students as a rule. One of my colleagues . . ." But Kate did not listen to Milton, and out of the corner of an ear I heard her telling Chester about the bluebell woods on Kingscliffe, and how she and Gertrude had picked primroses beside the brook that trickled into the scum-green pond at the bottom of the orchard, and made cowslip chains in the June meadows and ridden home late from the fields on top of a wagon-load of sweet-smelling hay, swaying like a tall ship, behind the broad-backed, glossy Bollocks and Emma who wore gaily coloured woven caps with tassels over their ears to keep off flies. She had a gift, had Kate, for bringing scenes before you, and these happened to be true; it was when she got on to people that her fancy took wing.

The house at Nathan's Orchard, she informed Chester, was part of an ancient manor that had been destroyed by fire centuries ago, and was haunted by a woman in grey who walked about a sunken garden wringing her hands; sometimes, from a distance, people saw flames leaping from the roof and heard the fire's roar, but when they approached they found only the quiet, low roofs of Nathan's Orchard, shadows in the sunken garden and the gnarled and moonlit apple trees. According to the legend, the woman in grey had given birth to an illegitimate baby and thrown it on the fire; her dress had caught alight and

she had burnt to death, and set the whole manor ablaze. Ever
since, the place had been cursed, and never passed from father
to son; it had come to Kate's mother when the heir had been
killed in a cavalry charge in the Boer War, by an assegai; she
got a bit confused at this point between the Crimea and Majuba.
Chester did not notice, however; he was deeply interested in
ghosts and even more in curses, so familiar in Greek tragedies,
and was quite carried away by her tale.

"The space-time continuum," Milton pronounced, "contains
the answer to these problems. Einstein has shown the way, now
it's merely a matter of how soon the human mind can compre-
hend and *arrange* these patterns. Those people really saw the
fire, they'd slipped into a different groove of time. Nothing that
ever happens is obliterated. One day we'll know the answers,
find the formulae."

"If the day ever comes when there's no mystery in life,"
Chester objected, "life will wither away because there'll be no
point in living. Mystery makes us wonder, wonder is life.
Without it we should be like people with all our food spread on
the table, and no appetite."

"I don't agree," Milton said. "The purpose of life is to
discover, and then to use what we discover wisely." "What is
wisdom?" Chester asked. "Given the freedom to ask questions,
maybe it's the ability to apply the answers with self-discipline
and moderation in the interests of mankind." Chester disagreed.
"To pursue the unattainable, that's the only happiness. What
we attain turns to dust."

He was coming back to Margaret, in a roundabout way.
"That wretched woman who threw her bastard on the fire,"
Kate inquired, "was she pursuing the unattainable? And did it
make her happy?" "She attained what she pursued, in a way,
that was her trouble." "She didn't pursue having a bastard, did
she?" "She may have done, unconsciously," Milton said, coming into line, surprisingly, with Chester. "There are psychologists who argue that the desire to have a baby is the true
motivation of all women's sexual activity." "Well I'll be
damned," Kate exclaimed. "Do psychologists really say things
like that? They must be stark staring mad." "I guess they
mostly are," Milton agreed.

Kate looked again at Chester. "What have you attained that turned to ashes?" "I've never attained anything much. Perhaps I never shall. Perhaps that's my trouble." "You don't look as though you had a lot of trouble." Chester laughed. "I've had my troubles. For instance when I was supervisor of female cashiers at the Wembley amusement park."

"You must teach me your secret sometime, Chester," Kate said.

"I haven't got a secret. I'm transparent as a piece of tracing paper." "You play with fire and don't get burnt." "If I have a secret, I've already told you. Pursue the unattainable." "There's a catch somewhere," Kate said. "Everyone does that, so everyone ought to be happy as kings but they're not." "That's because they won't admit in advance they'll never attain what they pursue. That's their mistake. Galahad never expected he'd really find the Holy Grail so he searched perfectly happily. If he'd found it . . ." "That's like saying you should start out to catch a train when you know it's already left the depot," Milton protested. "Well, maybe you should. It would save a lot of fuss and bother and probably a lot of wasted journeys."

"You're just too slippery," Milton said. "You know that's all boloney." I could see he was disgusted with this old-world sophistry, and Kate was looking tired. Chester had done her good, however; something in her had been deadened and now there was a stir of life again. We made our way by trolley to the sorority house where Mrs. Dimple brewed us camomile tea from an old New England recipe; oddly enough, we all enjoyed it. "I'll see you again before you leave," Chester said to Kate. "I thought of going tomorrow." "Why, no, you mustn't do that," Mrs. Dimple protested. "You stay until you're really rested. The girls so much enjoy your visit, they'll be mad if you leave." "You've all been very kind," Kate said.

Chapter Twenty

KATE stayed several days longer, growing restless. Although everyone liked and made a fuss of her, campus life began to pall. The point was, where was she to go? Julio, I gathered, had collected up his ties and vanished. Shamus was still at the Algonquin. "He's expecting me there," Kate said offhandedly, but we both knew that he was not.

"I wonder whether Uncle Alex would sell another horse," I suggested. "Why on earth should he?" "He sold a horse to get me here. He might sell another, quite a cheap one this time, to get you home." "Who said anything about my going home?" "You can't live the rest of your life in third-rate New York hotels," I pointed out. "I might work my way up to a second-rate one." "I do wish you'd face up to things *occasionally*, Kate." Kate laughed. She had won, and got her rise.

Two days later, I went round to the sorority house at four o'clock and found her gone. Mrs. Dimple handed me a note. "Thanks a lot for everything. See you one of these days. Watch your step with all those Big Red Guys." She gave no address.

"Such a sweet, *good* person," Mrs. Dimple commented. "Just *naturally* good. I can see how she would be, raised by those lovely nuns in that historic old convent where St. Hildegarde found her martyrdom. My, my. I reckon the nuns knew their business, to say Kate has a true Vocation; but then she's right too, there's more good to be done outside an Order than within it, unless you have the Gift of Grace. But little Kate will attain that, you mark my words. Her family must be very proud of her." "Yes, indeed." "Though it will be a great anxiety to them if she gains her ambition and goes to nurse lepers in the New Hebrides. She was delighted with my recipe for camomile tea."

Chester came round not long after, and took me out to dinner; he had been working hard to complete his course on hogs, while simultaneously translating Aeschylus' *Eumenides*.

"Did Kate tell you I took her down to New York City?" he asked. "*You* did? Why?" "She was going to thumb a ride. It's not a good idea to thumb a ride, not for a girl on her own. And Kate's not as hard-boiled as she makes out." "What did you do with her in New York?" "Margaret's got an aunt who lives in Yonkers so I left her there." This was quite a new light on Chester, acting so decisively; perhaps a relic of his naval days.

"I doubt if Kate will stay long in Yonkers," I suggested. "Well, it's a port in a storm. Meanwhile I rang up that fellow Shamus and gave him a piece of my mind." My amazement grew. "Did he listen?" "He rang off, but not before I'd told him he must buy her a ticket home and post it to Yonkers or I'd have his name blazoned in six-inch headlines all over London and New York. I'm afraid I told a fib, I said Kate had tried to chuck herself out of a window and left a note blaming him; I hauled her back just in time, but she'd try again if he didn't do as I said." "Good heavens, you're as bad as she is." Chester smiled. "Anyway it worked. Margaret's aunt rang up to say she'd got the ticket. Tourist class, but still." "I only hope she uses it," I said.

I did not know how to thank Chester; he had cut through all the knots so simply, yet he owed her nothing, and had never seemed the kind of man who liked to organize other people's lives. "Kate's like me," he added. "She needs a kind of guiding light." "I think what she needs most is the love of a good man. She's done the fasting already." Chester nodded. "That's probably true. A banana split or a peach nut sundae?" "I think just a plain coffee ice cream." "You must come to Athens one week-end and meet Margaret. They're going to do the *Antigone* at Easter." "I'd like to very much indeed."

Somehow or other, I never did get to Athens. As the term wore on we all grew busier, the mark-fever mounted, prelim followed prelim, people sat up all night with wet towels and flasks of coffee; spring came suddenly, Commencement loomed and then Commencement came.

Commencement is the wind-up of the academic year when those successful in their finals don gown and mortar-board, often for the first time, to receive from the hands of the President the sheepskin—a scroll—that is the pledge of triumph and the key to a career. There are speeches, songs, orations, Latin quotations; students wander round the campus with perspiring parents, sisters and kid brothers in tow looking at it as if for the first time, knowing it to be the last, at least *in statu pupilari*; suddenly those four years are telescoped into a fleeting moment; a door shuts, another is about to open onto an unknown, perilous world where you have your own way to make and only your own two feet to stand on. Suddenly the future is on top of you, starting tomorrow, instead of something distant, vague and full of glories. What if it should be full of flops? Not that, in this summer of 1928, there seemed much to fear; like the expanding universe of the astronomers, our world was inflating towards higher, better, brighter things. Our feet were on the escalator, going up; nothing could halt it. We were sixteen months exactly from the start of the Depression, and its seven or eight million unemployed.

With so much opportunity lying around like golden nuggets waiting to be picked up, it seemed silly to go back to an England whose nuggets had either been collected long ago or were reserved for those who had plenty already. There, the dawn came slow, so slowly, if indeed it came at all; here, the land was bright. It was not only a question of better opportunities to earn a living. America had hooked me. I wanted to stay on, probably for good.

I am not quite sure why; I was not sure then. American life, American attitudes, remained alien and by no means always admirable. There was more injustice, violence, cruelty and intolerance than in England, and much more crudity. I did not suppose that I had found Arcadia. The opposite, perhaps; here was challenge. In Europe, the hard bone of challenge had degenerated into a pulp of tradition and acceptance. Tradition smothered you, custom confined you, age and influence bound you as Gulliver was bound by Lilliputians. The class system—your school, your accent, your origin—governed all: not only your job and prospects but your life, your friends, your habits, what you could hope for—even the time of day you ate your meals. It forced you to conform. Everything was rigid, static, timid, smug: or so we thought—myself and thousands, millions even, of others. Europeans were flocking to the United States as fast as the quota would allow them in; there was a waiting list of five or six years from some countries, or even more.

It was not only those nuggets, which could be illusory. It was also the bigness of America, the sheer size. We derided Americans abroad for boasting of it, but they had seized upon the essential fact of their inheritance. Everything about their country was enormous—the landscape, the mountain ranges, the vast rolling forests, the immense plains. When rivers flooded they did not gently inundate water-meadows in which cows could stand hock-deep to avoid flies, but swept away entire towns, demolished levees, drowned beasts in tens of thousands. Even when erosion formed a gulley, it turned into the Grand Canyon. There was drama in everything.

Men had tried to match this with the works of their hand. They had made skyscrapers, gigantic dams, railroads that spanned thousands of miles built under scorching suns and through frozen snows by men whose lives had been cheap, rather than a branch line from Thaxted-upon-Ouse to Little Puddlecombe. They were still doing these things. The heroic age was not over, that was the difference. Mastery was incomplete.

And somehow all this bigness, we felt, had magnified the people, or at any rate the people's ideas. Dreadful things could happen to Americans but also they had noble hopes. Nobility was something England seemed to have given up, become afraid of, and so now mocked. On this continent it was still here, cohabiting with meanness, here in this land "Of tall corn, of wide rivers, of big snakes, of giants and dwarfs, heroes and clowns, grown in the soil of the mass of the people." "Precisely," Carl Sandburg went on to inquire, "who and what is the people?" He gave a lot of answers, including that of the alfalfa-land governor who said: "The common people is a mule that will do anything you say except stay hitched."

Of course a lot of this, we knew, was bunk. You did not need to be a geneticist to know that people were not created equal, nor a philosopher to realize that to base your political philosophy upon a falsity is rash, to say the least, even when it is expressed in such firm prose. (Thereby providing, as Bristow Adams pointed out, one of the minor ironies of history; in the event, no one apart from professional historians remembers much about what happened on the field of Gettysburg, but every American knows by heart what Abraham Lincoln said there.)

Here was an ideal that many waters had not quenched nor the floods devoured, struggling to find expression on a continent that seemed to hold everything between its oceans, great and dreadful, splendid and mean, cruel and kind—including hope, including the future. Here man's reach did indeed exceed his grasp, but he believed that he could grow longer arms.

Perhaps this is a grandiloquent way of saying that I wanted to stay in America because it was easier to get on. The question of employment was solved, like several others, by Bristow Adams. Before Commencement I had been employed in a branch of the extension services of the New York State College of Agriculture, which was attached to Cornell and under Bristow's general supervision. So I stayed on in Ithaca after the students had departed with their diplomas and degrees, their wardrobe trunks and 'coon-skin coats, their pennants and fraternity pins, their picture albums and victrolas and promises to write to friends, and all their hopes and good intentions.

It grew hot on the hill, the pavement burned your feet through sandals, after hours it was pleasant to swim in the creek, at night to walk about the quiet, deserted campus hoping for a cooling breeze, or sprawl on the terrace at Willard Straight and suck ice cream cones. By day I sat in the basement of the agronomy building writing chatty little news items mostly concerning some useful discovery intended to help farmers grow better crops more cheaply and with less toil, or to improve their livestock husbandry. The volume of these discoveries, emerging from Cornell itself and from other colleges, was astonishing, as was the number of weekly newspapers and other journals in the State into which they found their way. Mimeographing machines in the basement duplicated them in thousands and out they went in such a flow that every farmer in the State, you felt, should by now be cropping his land in the most up to date fashion possible and for the lowest cost. Experts designed his barns and byres for him, recommended the right machinery, analysed his soil, planned his crops, taught him accountancy, drew up feeding charts for fatting beasts, advised about sprays and fertilizers, dips and veterinary medicines, demonstrated how to pack his goods for market, informed him of the daily fluctuation in prices: and all free. It was a most efficient service and unmatched by anything in Britain, so far as I knew, or indeed in the rest of the world.

Bristow looked in from time to time to keep an eye on things and leave behind some aphorism for our edification. "It is impossible to over-estimate the ignorance of the public, but easy to under-estimate their ability to draw a sensible conclusion once they know the facts," was one. In writing, he had several quirks and foibles for which he could not account: if he came upon "for instance" he always changed it to "for example", and "a lot" always became "many". He himself fed into the service a constant stream of recipes and household hints. There could have been no more easy-going, agreeable and friendly boss, and in an unflurried, relaxed way everything ran smoothly and we never failed to get our copy out on time.

I could have stayed on happily for years in Ithaca but the regulations forbade it. I was on a student's permit, good only for a year. To stay on, I must first go back to England, enter my name on the quota and await my turn to emigrate. So, before the fall colours drenched hillsides and gorges, I had to pack my bags, sadly say goodbye to the friends remaining on the campus, and depart. This was to be only a temporary parting. I would be back; Bristow had promised to fix for me a job on one of the upstate newspapers, probably in Albany or Buffalo. That was the right way to start. There would be no difficulty. The world that was my oyster was already half open, and I could see the gleam of pearls inside.

Chapter Twenty-one

ONCE again, everything looked smaller; my eye had re-adjusted to a continental rather than an insular scale. It soon adjusted back. There was Nathan's Orchard, the garden a tangle of michaelmas daisies and golden-rod, apples glowing redly among twisted branches, everything green except the stubble which was golden. Most of the dung-heap had been carted so you could approach the back door. Piglets scurried about, rootling everywhere; speckled hens cackled with the satisfaction of concealing their eggs in broken carts, under heaps of straw, in hay-racks and the harness-room, anywhere but in the egg-boxes provided. Slabs of golden butter, criss-crossed by Scotch hands and stamped with swans and thistle-heads, lay in the dairy where Nellie still swung the brass-hooped barrel churn. Her uncle had died, she told me, so in the summer Perce had taken her to Bournemouth instead. Perce's knee had gone rheumatic, and he needed looking after; Aunt Madge had decided it would be suitable if he and Nellie married and she moved into his cottage, continuing to come and boil up the dogs' tripe, whose smell still pervaded the house.

I had the same small room at the end of the passage, next to the old nursery, which was empty now and used as a depository of things that might come in useful one day: cracked leather riding boots, a broken pram, egg-boxes, dog medicines, Uncle Jack's medals, a fruit spray, trunks of old clothes. It smelt strongly of onions, which made me recall nursery teas of bread and dripping and spring onions, or mustard-and-cress grown on a piece of flannel between two soup plates in the kitchen. The toys had long since been given away, but in the bottom of a cupboard I came upon some torn old painting-books and playing cards, and a chocolate-box full of tattered paper figures cut out of magazines.

They were all advertisements for women's fashions: tea-gowns, evening dresses, coats and skirts, Ascot dresses, *peignoirs*, tennis frocks, hats, *negligées*—anything wearable for any occasion, carefully snipped out of magazines by Gertrude. A small slit in or near the neck of each cut-out had enabled her to slip it over another paper figure, bringing about a change of dress. She would clothe her dummy in a dozen different outfits, each appropriate to the time of day or to some fashionable event—now a shooting party on the moors, now an evening at the opera, now a romantic assignation in a *boudoir* clad in a *peignoir*. Clothes had always fascinated Gertrude. This game had bored Kate, who liked something more active; she had painted, or made plasticine animals, or re-arranged things she had collected like birds eggs or shells, or encouraged old Sullivan to tell stories about colleens and leprechauns. Or sometimes she would wander off and, as Nellie said, put her nose into things. She always knew more than anyone else about what was going on; the postman's wife had had a baby, Nellie had left a pie too long in the oven, a fox had got into Ted's mother's poultry-run, a moorhen was nesting on the pond.

It was true that Kate's name must not be mentioned in front of Uncle Jack. But Aunt Madge had travelled to London, a very rare event, to see her and they had met at the Army and Navy Stores.

"I could have got her a good position as companion to Helen Armstrong-Tyrrell," my aunt said. "Her great-nephew married Jack's sister's niece. She's a great character—must be nearly ninety I suppose—and used to know everyone; Gladstone made her husband Ambassador to Japan and he translated Virgil into Chinese. She had a *salon* in her day. People don't have *salons* any more. It would have been a splendid opportunity for Kate to have met interesting people and learnt something of the world, but she thinks she's seeing life in these abominable night-clubs. All she's seeing really is a lot of very dull, stupid people with too much money spending it on trying to conceal their dullness and stupidity from themselves. However, she seems to have got quite a suitable job to do with art, she paints flowers on cups and trays and things for Harrods, and now she's living with a woman Miss Hapgold very strongly recommended, so I suppose she'll be all right."

Aunt Madge gave me Kate's address and also that of my youngest cousin Joanna, whom Aunt Kitty had removed from the spartan school in Suffolk to a much more congenial academy near Lausanne. Aunt Madge went through the motions of resenting Joanna's divorce from her own family, describing her sister as a baby-snatcher, or a serpent who had lured away her cherished offspring with a bait of gold. "After all I've done for that child!" she would exclaim. "To have one's own daughter *stolen*! But then, Kitty never had a thought for anybody's feelings but her own. With her money she can do what she likes. Money! It corrupts everything. Poor Joanna, even she will be corrupted . . ."

In her heart, I am sure that Aunt Madge was thankful not to have to cope with a teenage daughter so contaminated by foreign ways that she read novels in French, spurned a proper cooked breakfast, liked garlic in salads, wore flimsy shoes and was frightened of animals, including dogs. Moreover she had been heard to pronounce the name of the cinema in Otterbourne as Tée-vo-lee. "Affected brat!" my aunt had snorted. I only saw her once or twice before she married, not a foreigner as everyone had gloomily predicted—a fate if not worse than, at least as bad as, death—but a versatile young Scot with aesthetic rather than heathery tastes, who painted in water colours and became an authority on Italian literature; on an Italian island they lived on wine and olives and fish caught that morning, made friends with Axel Munthe and Norman Douglas, and sustained an enviable, sun-encompassed life until the Nazis destroyed it.

Gertrude was not at Nathan's Orchard either; she had more or less moved over to Boscombe these days. I borrowed the pony trap next morning and drove over myself, to find her in the flower-room surrounded by dahlias and chrysanthemums and a lot of bowls and vases, and seeming to be rather on edge. She gave me a peck on the cheek and said: "Hello, coz, good to see you back. Pity you couldn't have brought along a nice plump sugar daddy or two, one for you and one for me." "And p'raps another for Kate." "Oh, Kate . . ." Clearly Kate had been expunged from Boscombe as well as from Nathan's Orchard. I did not suppose that she would mind.

"How's Oliver these days?" Before I finished the sentence, I realized that I had made a dreadful *gaffe*. Gertrude seemed to freeze, there was an icy silence, and then her hands resumed their sorting out of dahlias with mechanical precision. She kept her hands white and soft and perfectly manicured.

"Why this sudden concern for Aunt Lilli's relations? I thought you despised them all from your exalted height."

"It's the other way round I should think. I just asked."

"Well, if your heart throbs for Oliver, you're too late. I believe he's engaged."

"Oh." There seemed no more to be said, except "Who to?"

"A girl, oddly enough. Actually I think you met her at Montleven, at that dreary dance you so much disliked. She was making eyes at old George Fulbright who's old enough to be her father, and trying to catch poor Tony at the same time. At least Tony avoided *that*."

"Oh, yes, Ruth, the girl who skated. She was very——" I had been going to say attractive, but stopped in time. "Rich, isn't she?"

"Don't ask me, I don't know anything about her. She's related to the Sebag-Montefiores, I believe. If you're so interested you'd better go and see them all in London. What *are* you going to do?" I told her I was going to look for a job that would support me until my turn came on the quota to go back to the States.

October was something of an in-between month for Gertrude; people were settling in after shooting birds and deer in Scotland, and preparing to pursue foxes; Gertrude was busy making and altering clothes. But Boscombe, Aunt Lilli said, would soon liven up again.

"Such an *interesting* man is coming down next week to enliven our rustic seclusion," she announced. "Not one of your callow youths with no ideas in his head except killing animals and no conversation. This is a Man of Affairs, one of those mysterious people who control our lives although most of us don't even know of their existence. One of the men behind our statesmen and diplomats, the wizards of finance and barons of industry. Shares rise and fall in millions at a mere nod from one of their sage heads. At the same time he's interested in the theatre, opera, in books and painting, all the pleasures of the intellect. We must cast aside our country bumpkinism and take

flight into the higher reaches of the mind, like dragonflies
emerging from slime with glittering wings. Gertrude, we shall
depend on you to charm our guest, to draw him out, not only to
feast his eyes but to nourish his mind."

"Hadn't you better shut up the parrot?" Miss Harriet, like
Gertrude, now made its home at Boscombe, the old countess
having died.

"Miss Harriet knows her friends from her foes. Sir Felix is
not a slaughterer of birds, in fact he is a *lover* of birds. Miss
Harriet will sense that immediately."

"Sir Felix?"

"A name to conjure with in the chancelleries of Europe but so
agreeable and easy, you'd take him for a simple soul devoted to
growing roses, enjoying music and supporting charities—he's
the most *generous* of men. A great tragedy befell him, he lost
his adored wife and now, though he presents a brave face to the
world, I believe *au fond* he's lonely and disconsolate. We must
console him as best we can in our rural surroundings."

"He doesn't sound as if the cub-hunting would be quite his
cup of tea."

"He would shrink from such brutalities. At all costs we must
keep him and nunc apart as much as possible. We must steer
clear of argument. Naturally Sir Felix wants to do away with
those wicked reparations and has many friends in Germany, and
talk of bloody Huns and the only good Germans being dead ones
would not delight him."

"I suppose he's middle-aged and bald and fat," Gertrude
observed.

"But *wealthy*. The day will come when the only riches to
matter will be the riches of the spirit; meanwhile, in this imper-
fect world . . . And so *kind*. He has gone to endless trouble to
help your cousin Oliver get a start in the world. With his con-
nections . . ."

Aunt Lilli broke off because Gertrude jumped to her feet and
ran from the room without a word, like a bolted rabbit. Even
Aunt Lilli was silenced for a moment. Then she shook her head.

"Our poor Gertrude! The wound is very slow to heal. It was
all most unfortunate. Wholly unsuitable of course, out of the
question. Oliver has his way to make in the world. I'm afraid my

nephew is a breaker of hearts. I wish Gertrude could reconcile herself . . . The time has come, my child, when we must *rescue* Gertrude. With our little spears and daggers, we must rush into the fray and deliver Gertrude from the prison-house of unrequited love. We must turn her thoughts in other directions."

"You mean Sir Felix?"

"I've always believed an older man would make Gertrude happier than one of our gilded sprigs. A mature, reliable, kindly *trunk* of a man rather than a sprig. He would be indulgent, generous, wise; she would reward him with beauty, youth and a mind that he could mould."

"He'd better not go near Nathan's Orchard," I remarked.

"Good gracious, I should think not! We must lock the doors on all the family skeletons and be careful not to upset nunc in any way. I shall invite in a few friends and neighbours . . ." Few of them, I thought, if any, would have much to say of interest to Sir Felix, but some of them had titles and large chunks of land, and might have relations in the Government. You never knew that someone's cousin might not be President of the Board of Trade, or married to an ambassador. Poor Gertrude was disgusted by it all.

"Aunt Lilli's like one of those disgusting old match-makers they used to have, mating people like animals for a few shillings. What does she think I am, a heifer sent to market? Really she's obscene. I shan't stay here any longer. There must be *some* kind of job I could get. Dress-making, I can do that, or perhaps they'd take me nursing lepers in Africa. Kate's managed it, she's got away. She may be a black sheep but she's got more guts than I have. Being a white sheep, or more or less white, speckled possibly, doesn't get you anywhere unless you've got money. Money, money, money. That's the beginning and end."

I had never seen Gertrude in such a state before and there was nothing I could say to console her; it was all true. "You'd better have a look at the good Sir Felix before you go off to nurse lepers," I suggested. "He *might* not be bald and fat. They still arrange marriages in France and people say they're much more successful than we are. You have lovers on the side and no one minds."

"Well, you try it," Gertrude said, "and tell me what it's like."

When I went out to the stables to harness Buttercup, Uncle Rufus was in a loose-box rubbing down one of his horses with fistfuls of straw. Here, at least, nothing had changed; the big cobbled courtyard, sluiced down with water still drawn in wooden buckets from a well; double doors with the patrician, glossy heads of hunters poking out of them; a smell of ammonia, leather and dubbin; halters and bridles hanging from pegs; saddles on frames, the rattle of buckets, stamp of hoofs and occasional neigh or whinny. Uncle Rufus looked as mottled and as gnarled as ever, hard of muscle and monosyllabic of tongue; here in the stables he was at ease, unruffled, safe from parrot and mockery. The clock in the tower had stopped at five past eight and a shiny, dark-red Daimler stood in one of the carriage-houses; a coupé, with a mascot in the shape of a fox-hound on the radiator. Uncle Rufus nodded briefly when I approached him, continuing to rub down his steed, assisted by a young strapper, who chewed a length of straw and hissed continuously like a snake.

"Hello, Kate," he said.

"Actually I'm not Kate."

"Don't know my own bloody nieces these days."

"I'm the one who's been in America."

"America, huh? See the Statue of Liberty?"

"Well, coming and going." My uncle straightened his back, wiping his hands on some straw.

"Better blister her tomorrow, huh," he remarked.

I could think of no reply to that, so remained silent, not quite liking to go. A grimace which I took for a smile passed over Uncle Rufus's face. "Had a Yank out two seasons ago. Said he had a pack of hounds in the States. Didn't go too badly. Get any hunting?"

"I'm afraid not."

Uncle Rufus always gave me the same feeling: he wanted to establish Natural Intercourse but had no idea how to go about it.

"I suppose you never play Fox any more," I said.

"All grown up now, huh. Never tell one from the other."

"Is it true that Ralph's going to ride in the Grand National?"

"Might get a ride, huh." We stood in silence for at least two minutes, as if on Armistice Day. I broke it awkwardly. "I must get back, I suppose."

Uncle Rufus nodded and grimaced again; a sense of shared relief was in the air. "Goodbye, Sybil."

The trees were turning now in hedgerow and spinney and on the slopes of Kingscliffe, where the bracken was a golden bronze; the earth smelt moist and fruity, hawthorn berries glowed scarlet in the hedges, spindleberries were white as snow, everything was lush and tangled in the orchards and by the side of the road. Three Sundays had gone by after horse-drawn binders had clanked round, so most of the corn had been carted, but rows of stooks remained in some of the fields. Men were up on ladders thatching ricks, fixing neatly in the little pegs to which they tied bundles of thatching straw. Poultry houses had been towed out to the fields so that the hens could support themselves by gleaning; piglets were rootling in the stubble. Coveys of young partridges took off and landed at a safe distance; now and again a cock pheasant strutted across the road.

Autumn was a splendid time, but I did not mean to stay at Nathan's Orchard. Analysing pastures at Aberystwyth for my keep but no pay was so far the only job I had been offered, but I was going to London to see what I could find. Meanwhile, I had arranged to meet Dando for a gossip in Exeter, which both of us could reach by bus. Jumbo was in training somewhere in Scotland. I could not see him as a very dashing pilot, but no doubt it was best not to be too dashing in the air.

Chapter Twenty-two

THE telephone had been installed on a table outside Uncle Jack's study and he was supposed to hear the bell. Sometimes he did, but that was not the same as answering its summons. The messages it bore were few but mostly detrimental, such as people suggesting themselves for tea, the station to say something was there to be collected, or reminders about overdue accounts; so the telephone was seldom answered. After a while it had become well-trained, and seldom pealed. It was something of a fluke, therefore, that Dando got through the day before our rendezvous.

"I can't come tomorrow."

"I'm sorry. Nothing wrong, I hope?"

"Well, there is rather."

"Oh, dear. Not Patch, I hope?"

"No, not Patch. But——" There was an odd kind of grunt, and then silence. "Hello, are you there?"

"I'll write." That was all.

I felt uneasy; it was not like Dando to be thrown off her stride. No letter came next morning, and by the time it did come, I knew what was in it. South Molton was not far away and the bush telegraph efficient. Jumbo had crashed in Scotland and been killed.

Although he was not a frequenter of Nathan's Orchard, the news cast a gloom. "People who play about with inventions of the devil," Aunt Madge said, "must expect to get killed." "Thank God there's still enough spirit of adventure left in this country," Uncle Jack responded, "to inspire young fellows like Matheson." "It's not much use being inspired by the spirit of adventure if you merely get killed." "Blood is the price of admiralty," Uncle Jack quoted. "I wonder what his mother will do."

I wondered what Dando would do. She had had her one and only chance. Nothing but bloodhounds from now on—and Patch, so long as he lived. He was middle-aged.

Aunt Madge could be very unexpected. "Why don't you ask that girl here for a few days?" she said to me.

"You mean Dando?"

"I suppose she'll be coming over to see old Mrs. Matheson. She could come on here."

"That's very good of you, Aunt Madge. I'll suggest it." To my surprise, Dando accepted, having been granted compassionate leave from her cheese factory near Yeovil. She looked just the same; grief had not thinned her down but perhaps it had made her less self-conscious, more indrawn. Uncle Jack took to her immediately. "Not a chatterbox, thank God." "Sensible boots," Aunt Madge commented. She took Dando off on long tramps to exercise the terriers. Dando did not flinch from wading waist-deep in Kingscliffe bracken; she never forgot to put each dog on a lead when crossing a road, and understood at once how much boiled tripe was appropriate for each terrier. "They seem like toys after the bloodhounds," she remarked, "but they're nice little beggars all the same."

"I'm sorry you didn't bring Patch."

Dando frowned and looked away; her face shut up like the door of a safe. "Mrs. Matheson took him." I supposed that Jumbo's mother had wanted him as a memento. When Dando was not engaged upon canine business, Uncle Jack invited her into his study to help him to transcribe his notes on the Ashanti campaigns.

"It's you who ought to be doing this, really," Dando told me. "I'm no fist at slinging words about."

"I'm no authority on the Ashanti campaigns."

"They're a sort of blind actually. Only don't say I said so."

"What do you mean, a blind?"

"Well, he's really writing stories."

This was a new light altogether on my uncle. "What sort of stories? About wars and frontiers and things?"

"No, not like that." Dando looked embarrassed. "Though one of them does have a wounded soldier in it. Some of them are in the South Seas, and some in ancient Egypt, and there's one on the planet Venus."

"I'd no idea Uncle Jack had so much imagination. Are they love stories?"

Dando wriggled and averted her eyes. "I suppose you could call them that. They're very, well, outspoken."

"He reads them to you?"

"With a great deal of feeling. For goodness' sake don't mention this to a soul. I shouldn't have told you really, he doesn't want anyone to know."

The sad thing was, that no one would have been interested, least of all Aunt Madge. She was more than ever in Perce's company. Perce nowadays frequented the drawing-room more often than the kitchen; the springs of Uncle Jack's arm-chair had broken and the dogs had taken it over. Perce left his boots outside the back door and went about in stockings as if in a mosque; he was rheumaticky, and walked more slowly, his dark face was more deeply lined, but his manner had not changed: independent and respectful. In his presence Aunt Madge was more mellow, sometimes almost arch. If a dog was ill it was Perce, not Uncle Jack, who would sit up all night with it. Aunt Madge retired early and once or twice, passing her bedroom door at a late hour, I heard Perce's gruff, slow tones from within. It was understood that, in due course, he would settle down with Nellie, but no one was in a hurry. Things rubbed along all right, more or less, as they were.

In London, I found temporary accommodation in a small back room in a dingy house off Ennismore Gardens where a distant cousin on my father's side took in girls, and gave music lessons to such pupils as could be found.

Cousin Winifred dressed in long, unfashionable skirts with long-sleeved blouses, held herself upright as a poker, kept everything spotlessly clean however shabby, and served up for her lodgers' breakfast every morning a dish of porridge which she expected them to sprinkle salt on and eat standing up, although she did also provide a sticky, black sort of sugar. My room, with such meals as I wanted, cost a pound a week.

I looked for a job and also for Kate, whom I eventually located. We met at a small restaurant in Soho where an excellent meal was to be had for half a crown, and a half-carafe of red wine for an extra two shillings. Kate looked less on edge than she had been in New York or Ithaca, and seemed quite gay.

"Are you really painting flowers on china?" I inquired. Kate looked puzzled. "Who said I was?" "I thought *you* did. Your mother said so." Kate laughed.

"So I did. It was an idea I had, I thought it might be fun, but it didn't materialize."

"What are you doing instead?"

"At the moment, I'm sort of housekeeper. That's to say I'm looking after two brothers in a studio flat in Chelsea. They both work very hard."

"What at?"

Kate flicked off her cigarette ash with what I took to be a nonchalant air. She wore her close-fitting hat on the back of her head and a neatly arranged curl on each temple, like small, flattened rams' horns. "I never ask questions, coz. Men don't like to be pinned down." She spoke airily. "One brother works during the day and the other at night, so it fits in very well as there's only one bed."

"What happens at week-ends?"

"Oh, we manage." Kate gave one of her silent laughs. "You ask too many questions. How are things at Nathan's Orchard? What's all this about Gert?"

I had not seen Aunt Lilli since the visit of Sir Felix to Boscombe, but had rung her up to say goodbye. She had put on a conspiratorial act. "Our little plot, my child, is *thickening*. I can say no more than that on the telephone. Things went even better than I had hoped. Our good knight appeared in shining armour and I do believe he positively *dazzled* our damsel in distress. You may be hearing of Developments. I can say no more."

I asked Kate whether she had met Sir Felix. "Actually yes, I lunched with him and Gert at Claridge's." I could not help but be impressed. "He's really not a bad old stick. He's got those liquid, ancient Jewish eyes, you know, that look as if they've seen everything."

"I daresay his have seen a good deal. How old is he?"

"Oh, fiftyish I suppose. He's got a grown-up daughter."

"Is he fat and bald?"

"Plump, but not bald—at least, he's got quite a lot of rather curly hair but it could be a wig."

"He doesn't sound wildly attractive."

"How many men are, coz, if you come down to it? He's clever as a cartload of monkeys and he isn't dull. And of course rolling. Gert could do a lot worse. He may be an old dog but there's life in him yet."

"Just what do you mean by that?"

Kate giggled. "Actually, he asked me to dinner with him at his flat, to see his modern paintings. They sound divine."

"Kate! You really *mustn't*."

She fiddled with her curls, quivering with laughter. You never knew with Kate: she might be pulling my leg. "Now I've got some news for you," she said. "A friend of yours is coming over from the States. Perhaps you know already."

I did not, and was astonished when she told me: it was Chester. He was arriving in a few days time.

"I didn't think he'd tear himself away from Margaret," I remarked.

"D'you believe Margaret really exists?"

"Of course. Don't you?" I had never questioned Margaret; so far as I knew, Chester was a truthful man—exceptionally so —and the story too unlikely to have been made up.

"Have you ever met her?" Kate inquired.

"No, but then I wouldn't. I didn't go to Athens."

"Well, you may be right. But Chester's feet are in the clouds, or do I mean head? As soon as he gets here we'll make a date." She insisted on paying for her share of the meal. "I come here quite a lot," she said.

"With the brothers?"

"Yes. Well, one at a time. They seldom overlap. You must meet them now you're going to be in London, they're very gay and full of ideas." On this cryptic note she waved and departed. She was dressed, out of character, in a well-cut tailor-made she had bought from Gertrude, who had been given it by one of her rich friends. Well-cut, expensive tailor-mades lasted practically forever if they were well looked after, and Gert looked after hers with such care that she took the skirt off when travelling in the second-hand Baby Austin she had managed to acquire, so as not to spoil its shape. Halted, on one occasion, by a constable for some minor traffic offence, she had stepped into a crowded street clad in a well-cut jacket and a pair of silk knickers. A crowd had begun to gather, and the constable had waved her on.

When one door shuts, another opens; although I did not know it, the door guarded by the Statue of Liberty had shut for me, thanks to the miscalculations of people like Sir Felix; by the time my name came up on the quota, the United States had five or six million unemployed, a great many stockbrokers were said to have leapt off skyscrapers, breadlines stretched for miles in every city, the great American dream of more and more of everything for everyone had exploded, and I stayed where I was. A small door had opened off Tothill Street admitting me from nine till six at four pounds ten a week, a salary about double that received by shorthand typists, and enabling me to move from cousin Winifred's to a bed-sitter in Pimlico. This was a back room too, no more spacious and costing thirty shillings a week, but there was no porridge, no communal meals and no cousin Winifred; I was at that stage of life when all relatives seem better avoided, at any rate all older ones.

My path and those of Kate and Gertrude were diverging. Gertrude invited me to the house of some friends in Halkin Street, and gave me a glass of excellent sherry. Her coat and skirt were impeccable, everything about her just right, she looked self-possessed and lovely and wore a diamond ring.

"A dreadful thing's just happened," she said. "Felix has telephoned to say he's held up by some stupid business thing and can't get round here. I did so want you to meet him. *Such* a blow. Of course he's devastated."

I knew she was keeping Felix and her relatives apart, very wisely, until the register was signed. "He's such a pet. I know he's old enough to be my father, but he's kind."

"That's everything."

"Very nearly everything. Of course he's rich too. I don't know anything about the things he does. It's all rather alarming. But fun."

"What are you going to do about Nathan's Orchard?"

"I've told him daddy's crippled with arthritis and mummy's a recluse and he's not pressing at the moment. I daresay Aunt Lilli has dropped hints; he's very tactful. Of course there's no question of a slap-up wedding, and anyway he doesn't want it;

he thinks it might upset his daughter. She's nineteen, and musical. So it's to be a registry office, then a honeymoon in Italy. You must come and see us when we get back."

"I'd love to." I knew I shouldn't, or perhaps just once, when they had moved into a house in Green Street. Felix might be going to stand for Parliament. I admired Gertrude tremendously for keeping her nerve. It must be like walking blindfold across a minefield and she had no one to take her hand. When I said, "I hope you'll be very happy," I meant it; and when she said: "I'm sure I shall," I believed her. She had buttered her bun and would lie on it with elegance as well as resolution. "Felix has insisted on my going to Molyneux for a trousseau," she said. "Isn't it exciting?" She glanced at her watch and I took the hint.

When I got back to Pimlico my landlady, looking arch, said: "You've a gentleman caller, been here since six." She was not one of those who objected to gentleman callers, so long as they behaved; she kept a respectable house but did not pry. So there was Chester, sitting on an upright chair in front of a non-ignited gas fire, and there on a bamboo table was the black homburg that always crumpled his right ear. His suit was as well brushed and pressed as ever, his chin as smooth, his eyes as clear and blue. We shook hands. I was pleased to see him and yet, as always with Chester, a little unsure; it was impossible to know what was going on in that world of his own.

"Kate told me you were coming over, it was a surprise."

"It all came on rather suddenly. There were complications about the apple farm I'd hoped to buy and anyway I didn't want to tie myself down indefinitely. So I'm thinking it over."

"I'm sure that's wise."

"That's what Margaret thought too. You can see things better from a distance, as she said. A sense of perspective."

"Yes."

"And then there's the question of your cousin Kate."

I offered him some sherry in a tooth-mug. "It's only a cheap kind I'm afraid, not awfully good." Chester would have paced the room had it been big enough; as it was, all he could do was to keep getting up and sitting down on the chair, while I sat on the bed.

"Am I my brother's keeper? You may ask—sister in this

case. Yes should be the answer. Yes. No man is an island, we are part of the main and so on. On the other hand, that may conceal a fallacy. Do I really know what's good for my brother? Or sister. I might make even worse mistakes. Almost certainly should. Perhaps we do less harm by making our own mistakes without trying to mop up after other people's."

I offered him more sherry. Unfortunately there was only one tooth-mug. "You were very good to Kate. If it hadn't been for you, I don't know what would have happened to her."

"Now and again, without expecting it, something suddenly opens up that you can *do*: action. And if it works out right then you're tempted to believe in fate."

"You think it was fate that made you rescue Kate from the jam she'd got into?"

"I had a feeling, when I met her, that I was there for a purpose if you know what I mean. It was such an extraordinary chance we met just at the moment when she needed the sort of help that I could give. It isn't often one can help people. It's a kind of debt you want to pay but as a rule there's no one to pay it to. I'm afraid I'm not explaining all this very well."

"One can't explain feelings; the point is one has them. You're feeling now you want to help Kate."

"I suppose that's what it boils down to. It sounds awfully priggish. Is it, d'you think?"

"I don't know. Kate's very independent. She may not want to be helped."

"Well, one can try. You know how, when you're riding, and lose the way, if you let the reins drop on the horse's neck it will generally find the way home. When I don't know what to do I drop the reins, so to speak, and up till now it's seemed to work. One day perhaps I'll see the map. I don't know." He gave me one of his attractive smiles. "You see, I think Kate's one of the few people I've met who's kept her integrity. Anyway I'm meeting her for supper and came along to ask you to come too."

The evening was full of surprises; he took me to a vegetarian restaurant, and when Kate arrived she was gay as a lark. We had fruit juice cocktails and ordered nut cutlets. "Do you think all this is very cranky?" Chester asked. "I *adore* nut cutlets,"

Kate said with real enthusiasm, not put on, and when they came she ate them with relish. "I've always wanted to be a vegetarian but no one else I know ever has, and it's too much effort on one's own. Now I can really let myself go." Chester looked delighted. Who would have suspected Kate of a suppressed desire for nut cutlets? Fate was weaving them together in ways too strange to be fortuitous. Looking at Chester, I thought suddenly of the engraving that hangs on so many walls of Watts's picture of Sir Galahad hacking with his sword at a rope securing a naked lady to a tree, both looking as embarrassed as the situation would demand of two well-bred young persons in the late Victorian age. While Kate bore no resemblance whatever to that naked lady, Chester was in the spiritual tradition of that chivalrous knight. Chivalry was a forgotten, lost and misprized quality, and here it was, cropping up again, to prove that nothing disappears but is only transmogrified; when no one can recognize the original, new names are found.

Chester said he wanted to return to Greece and translate the *Odyssey*, however many people had done so already. From Athens, New York, back to Athens, Greece—or rather not Athens but to Mount Athos, Delphi and Corinth, to Thebes, Lemnos and Skyros, and all those islands with the magic names: Samothrace and Mytilene and Thasos. He spoke of fishermen with dark curly hair and dark sunburnt bodies and dark living eyes, of women working in the vineyards, of clustering grapes, ripening olives, hot tawny rocks, scuttling lizards; of the smell of thyme, of cerulean skies, of wine-dark seas. Kate was enraptured. They would find a hovel in the hills above the sea and live on goats' milk and cheeses and on olives and wine; fish were questionable. Lax vegetarians winked at fish, but Kate and Chester agreed that they were animals and banned; eggs, however, were permissible.

It seemed to be agreed that they would go together to these enchanting places, starting more or less next day, abandoning the drab English winter that was coming on, wet streets and windy undergrounds and bus queues, Kate's Box-and-Coxing brothers and, presumably, Chester's upstate apple farm and conjectural Margaret. This was no moment for banal and boring questions, such as what would they live on, re-translating the *Odyssey* being, one would suppose, a labour of love rather than of profit.

"You must join us, coz," Kate invited; her eyes were bright, her smile gay and innocent. "We'll have a *ménage-à-trois*."

"You've got one already."

"This will be quite, quite different. Out of doors. Everything that's out of doors is different. There'll be a lemony smell and cicadas, the sea will be warm and silky and there'll be fields of asphodel, or do I mean amaranth? What *is* amaranth?"

"Immortal amaranth," Chester said. "The flower that never was. That blooms perhaps on Cythera, or the Isles of the Blest."

"What fat juicy words," Kate exclaimed. "One could eat them off the tree like ripe plums. When can we start?"

"We could start tomorrow."

"Why not? D'you mean it, Chester?"

"I mean it, Kate."

"I haven't any money."

"I've got enough to go on with. We shan't need much."

"All right then. Where shall I meet you?"

"Victoria Station. Say four o'clock."

"Is there really a train to take us to the fields of amaranth?"

"At any rate it will take us to Athens."

They were looking at each other now with a different expression, Chester gravely, Kate with a half-smile, quite absorbed, quite oblivious of the steamy restaurant and jostling waitresses, the smell of wet macintoshes and frying and tobacco smoke and coffee, the clatter and crumbs, and of my presence. Outside it was dark and raining with a cold and gusty wind but they were seeing fields of amaranth on Cythera where Aphrodite sprang naked from the foam, and purpling the slopes of the Delectable Mountains, and glowing in the meadows of the Land of Cockayne.

They did not leave next day, however, from Victoria station; Kate telephoned two or three days later. "There were passports and things. And Chester wanted to get a licence."

The word suggested dogs in January, but it was not January and they would hardly be taking a dog. A wireless? A car?

"A *special* licence. Can you imagine?"

"Oh. Why not? It sounds a splendid plan."

"Yes, but it's expensive. Chester says British consuls do it for next to nothing."

"Everything is cheaper abroad."

"So can masters of merchant ships, he thinks. They can bury people anyway."

"Cheaply too, I should imagine."

"So we're going by sea. A cargo boat sailing from Falmouth. I can't think what her cargo will be."

"Ivory, apes and peacocks."

"Peacocks have dreadfully harsh voices, shrieks you might say. I'll write from Athens."

"Yes, do."

"Chester sends his love."

"Give him mine too. What about Nathan's Orchard? I mean, does Aunt Madge know?"

"I don't think she'd be interested. If you see them, tell them I've gone to nurse orphans in China."

"I thought it was to be lepers in the New Hebrides."

"Either would do. Look after yourself, coz."

"Same to you."

We rang off simultaneously. A month or two went by before a postcard came, not from Greece, but from Egypt, showing the Sphinx and saying: "My window is marked with a cross. What amazing things camels are but it isn't true their bites go bad. Love to all." Chester also sent a postcard with a statue of Nefertiti, and inscribed: "There are fields of amaranth along the banks of the Nile."